D0885419

ART AND ANATOMY

ART AND ANATOMY

By Heidi Lenssen

Text edited by Lancaster M. Greene

BARNES & NOBLE, INC. • 105 Fifth Avenue • N. Y.

PUBLISHERS · BOOKSELLERS · FOUNDED 1873

B&N
1873

Reprinted by BARNES & NOBLE, INC.
Eighth Printing, 1964

L. C. Catalogue Card Number: 55-12083

MANUFACTURED IN THE UNITED STATES OF AMERICA

"Lo, the pulses of the man throb with the yearning of the God—he would aid in the process of the suns!"

HENRY GEORGE

Into this volume the author has attempted to compress the essentials of human anatomy needed by the artist. Bearing in mind that a knowledge of anatomy, however useful, is but one of the manifold experiences important to the artist's work, the author has tried to exclude all nonessentials. The doctor will desire many other details which the artist can afford to pass over.

"Art and Anatomy" is primarily for the artist who is portraying people—who is aware that all human expressions and motions are based upon the physical movements of muscles and bones, and who would like a source to which he can refer for ready information.

In addition, "Art and Anatomy" contains a carefully selected collection of reproduced drawings of masters who devoted much of their time to the study of anatomy. Albrecht Duerer, for example, studied anatomy many years, overcoming all the difficulties which beset the pioneer. Duerer was so fascinated by anatomy that for some time he neglected his creative work for this new science. Michelangelo, in the same period, devoted seven years of his life to anatomy, procuring bodies and dissecting them himself to learn the secrets of the human structure.

To the layman, this volume should be of much interest. "Art and Anatomy" will, it is hoped, give him a greater appreciation of the extraordinary structure which the Master Artist designed for the simple functioning of the human body.

Praying Hands

(Albrecht Duerer 1471-1528 *Courtesy of Erich S. Herrmann Inc.*)

BONAROTI

MAN CALLING (MICHELANGELO BUONAROTTI 1475-1564)

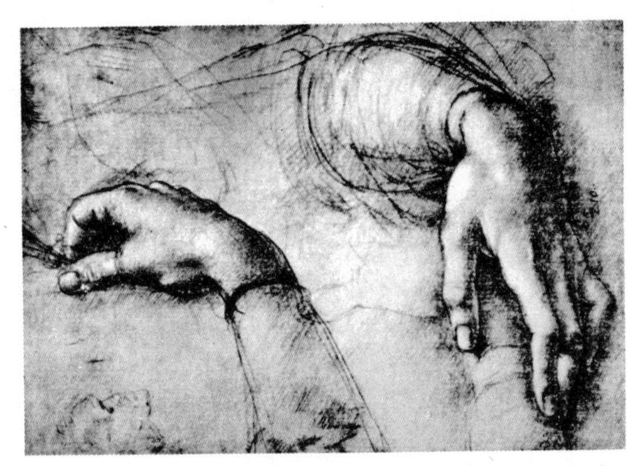

Study of Hands (Leonardo da Vinci 1452-1519)

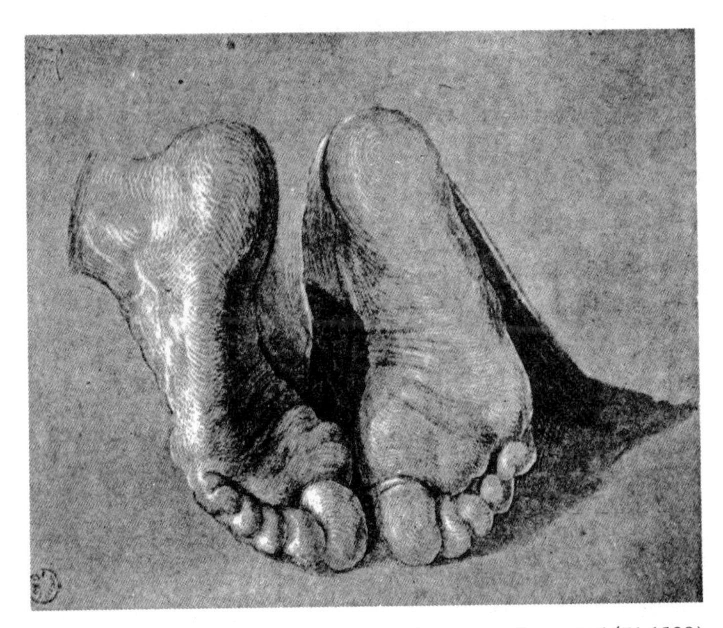

Study of Feet (Albrecht Duerer 1471-1528)

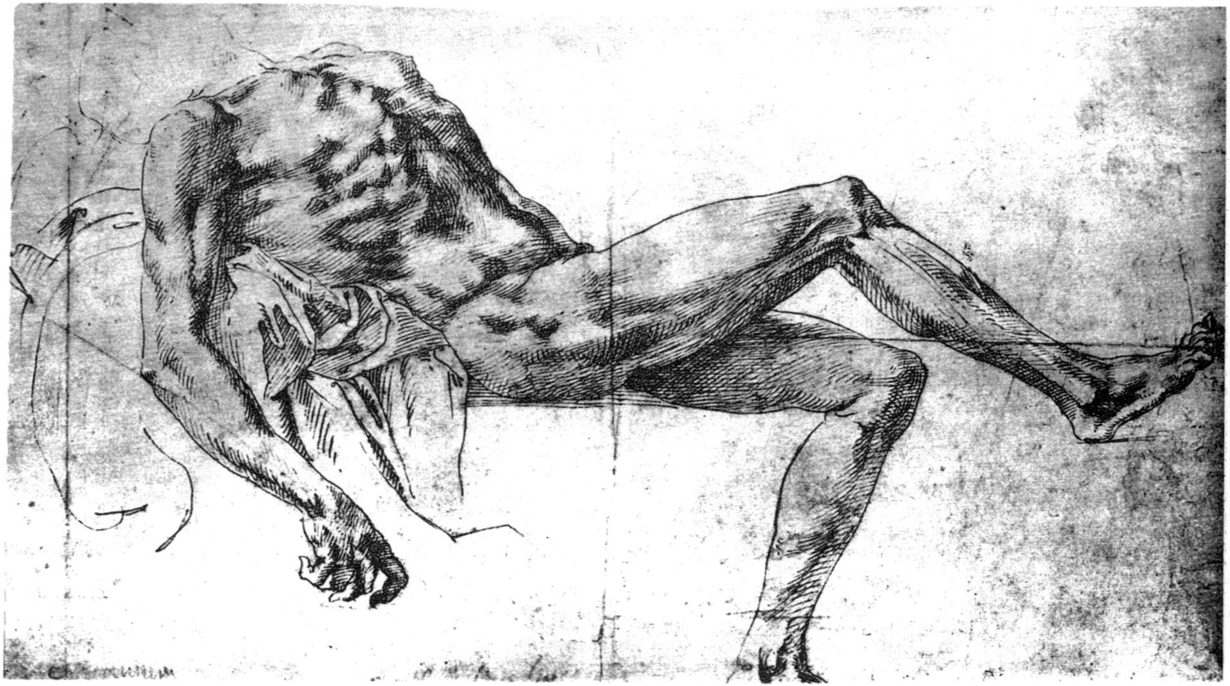

MALE NUDE

(MICHELANGELO BUONAROTTI 1475-1564)

Male Nude and Leg and Foot Studies
(Michelangelo Buonarotti 1475-1564)

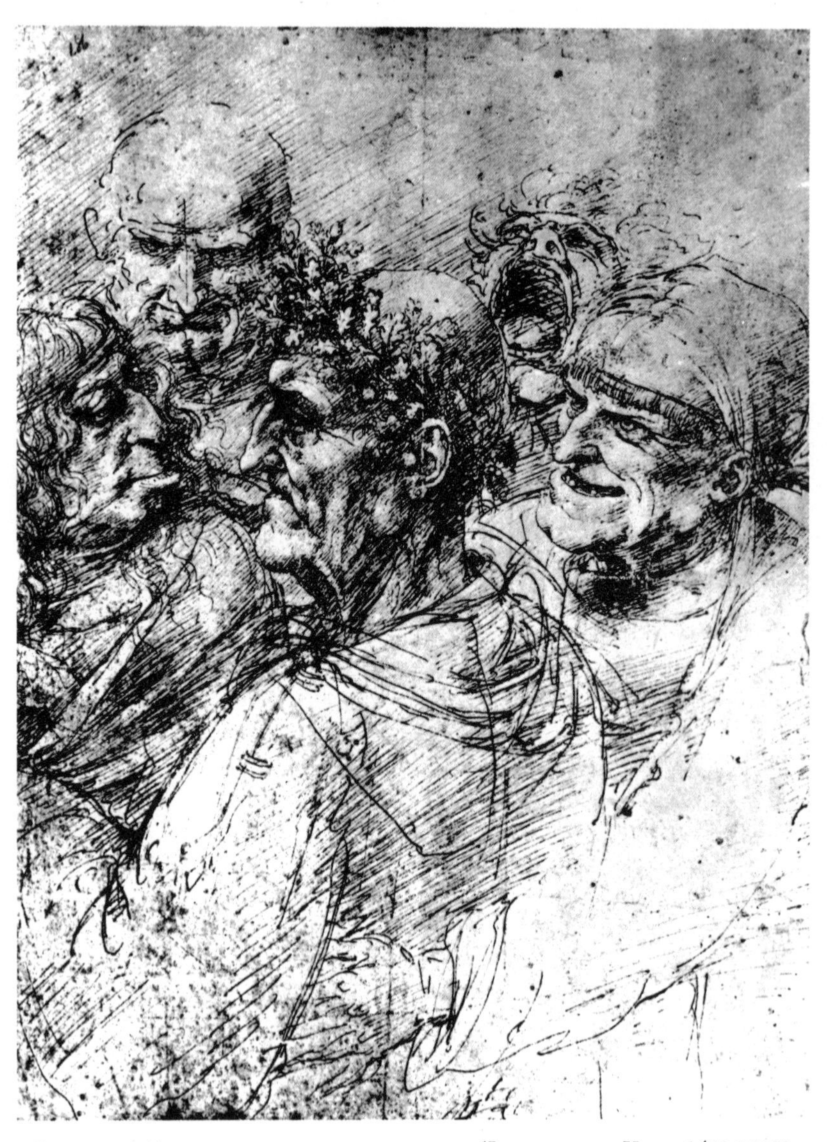

GROTESQUE FACES (LEONARDO DA VINCI 1452-1519)

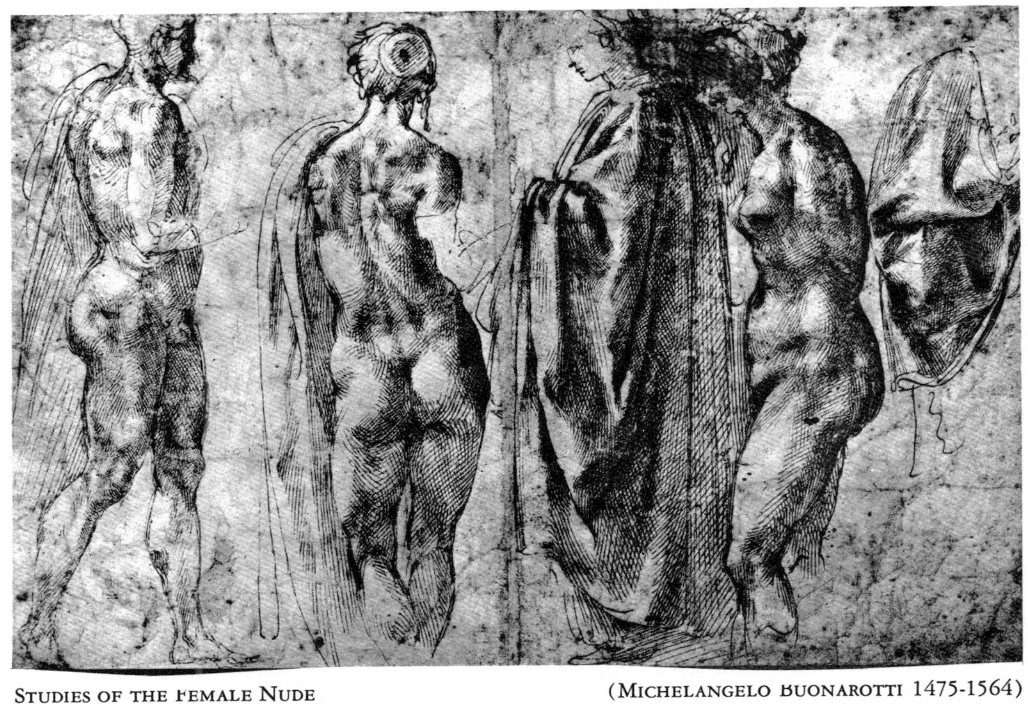

STUDIES OF THE FEMALE NUDE (MICHELANGELO BUONAROTTI 1475-1564)

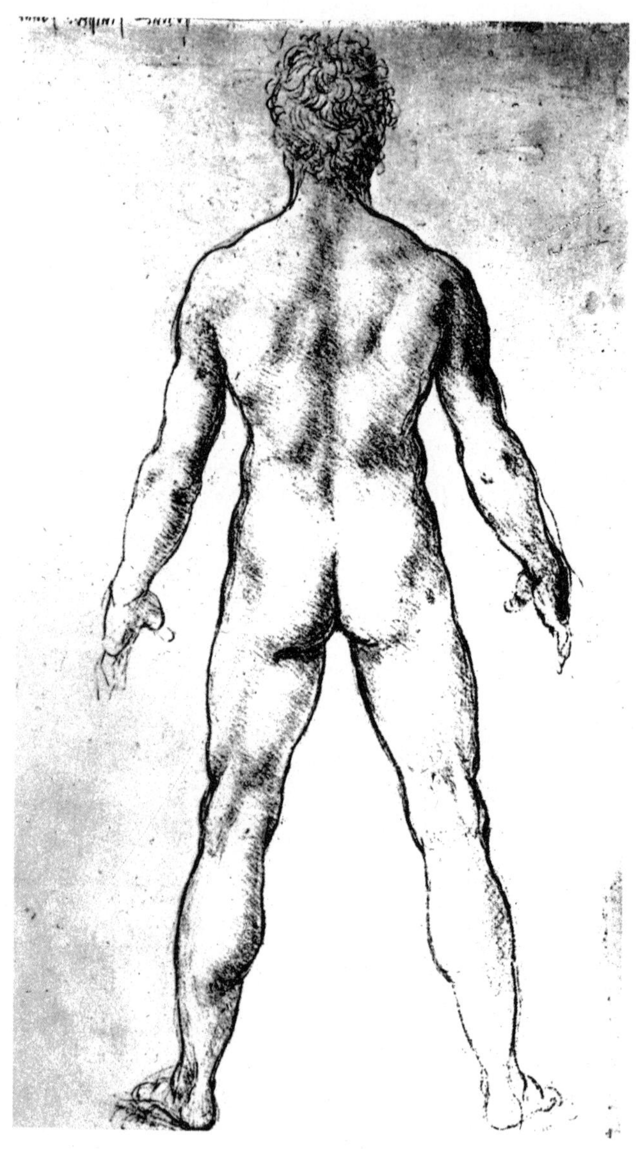

Male Nude (Leonardo da Vinci 1452-1519)

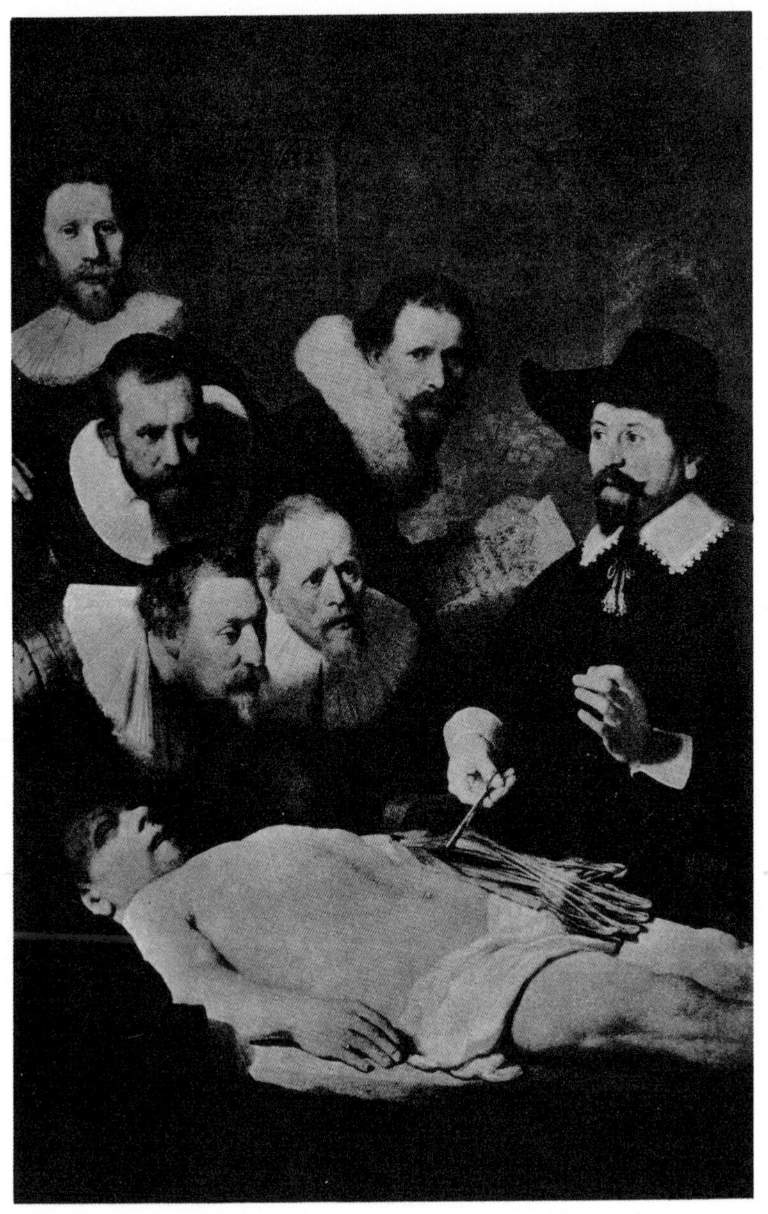

Detail from the Anatomical Lecture (Rembrandt 1632)

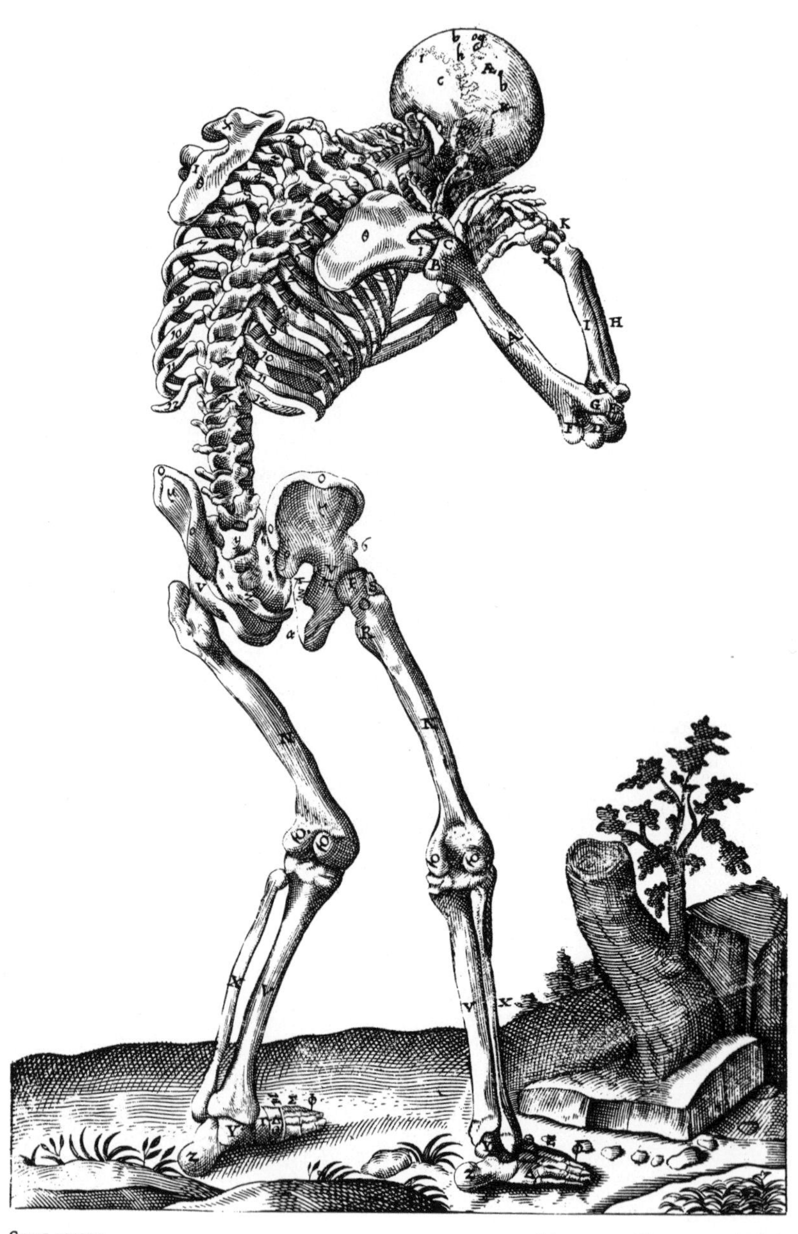

SKELETON (ANDREAS VESALIUS 1543)

Anatomical Study of a Female Nude

(George Grosz *Courtesy of H. Bittner and Co.*)

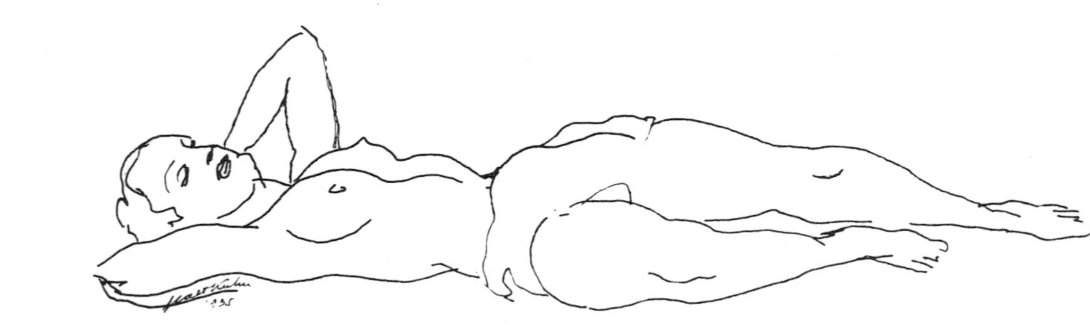

Sketch of a Female Nude (Walt Kuhn 1935)

Chapter I

BONES

The bones of the skull

The bones of the skull are the frontal, the parietal, the temporal and the occipital bones, which form the upper part of the skull. The face consists of: the nasal and the malar or cheek bones, which form the frame of the eyehole, together with the external and the internal angular process of the frontal bone and the superior maxillary of the upper jawbone. There is also the inferior maxillary or lower jawbone with its two angles of the jaw and the mentum or chin. The mouth cavity is formed by the upper and the lower jawbones.

The neck bones

The neck bones consist of the seven upper cervical vertebrae in the back and: the hyoid bone, thyroid cartilage, cricoid cartilage, trachea or windpipe, and the small thyroid body directly above the clavicle in front.

The bones of the thorax

The thorax or chest is formed by the sternum in front, the ribs and the vertebra column of the back, or the 12 dorsal vertebrae. The clavicle bone in front and the spine of the scapula in the back, in joining, form the shoulder. While in a resting position, the upper border of the shoulder blade or scapula follows the direction of the second rib, and the lowest point of the triangle, called scapula, moves toward the spine, if the arm is pressed against the body, and away from it, as the arm is being lifted upward. The scapula consists of: the base or vertebra border of the scapula, the root of the spine of the scapula, the spine of the scapula and the acromion process of the scapula, the latter embracing the head of the humerus—the bone of the upper arm.

Front of the thorax: The clavicle which has an S shape, even more pronounced than all the other bones of the human body—runs from the manubrium, or first piece of the sternum to the coracoid process of the scapula and by doing so covers part of the first rib. The rib cage or chest consists of the sternum in front (which in itself is composed of: the first piece or manubrium, the second piece or blade, the third piece or ensiform cartilage) and the upper seven ribs, named the true ribs, which are connected by their cartilages with the sternum. The five false ribs, so-called because they are either indirectly or not at all connected with the sternum, are the 5 lower ribs of the cage. Cartilages of the 8th, 9th and 10th ribs join cartilages of the ribs above; the 11th and 12th ribs are connected only with the spine in the back, and are therefore called floating ribs. The vertebral column is constructed of 24 vertebrae, which are grouped into seven cervical vertebrae, twelve dorsal vertebrae, and five lumbar vertebrae. The seven cervical vertebrae are topped by the atlas, which supports the occipital bone or base of the skull. The next lower vertebra is called the axis. The seventh, which is just above the first rib, is named the vertebra prominens, referring to its size. Then follow the 12 dorsal vertebrae which embrace the length of the thorax and at last the 5 lumbar vertebrae, which can be considered the bridge between the thorax and the pelvis.

The bones of the pelvis

The pelvis consists of the two hip bones and the sacrum and coccyx. The two hip bones are constructed of three parts: the iliac, the ischium and the pubic bones. The anterior superior iliac spine and the iliac crest are those parts of the bone which show most prominently in almost any position and in male and female alike. So do the two spots or dimples, in the back view, which are caused by the joining of the hip bones with the sacrum.

The coccyx represents the last bone of the spine. The whole unit of the pelvis—the hip bones and the sacrum and coccyx—form a bony girdle which is completely immovable between its several parts.

The arm bones

The upper limb or arm bones consist of the scapula, the humerus, or upper armbone and the ulna or elbowbone and the radius, the latter two forming the lower arm skeleton. The eight small bones, called carpus or wristbones, form the extremely flexible part of the hand, which we call the root of the hand. They bear the following names: scaphoid, semilunar, pisiform, cuneiform; (lower row): unciform, os magnum, trapezoid, trapezium.

The hand is composed of the metacarpus, or bones of the palm, and the phalanges, or bones of the fingers, which are subdivided into the first, second and third phalanx.

The leg

The lower limb or leg is composed of the femur or thighbone, the patella or kneecap, the tibia or shin bone and the fibula, which together form the bones of the lower leg. The upper end of the femur, which is connected with the hipbone, is called the great trochanter of the femur. The ankle of the foot is formed by the malleolus externus (the lower end of the fibula) and the malleolus internus, which is the lower end of the tibia or shin bone.

The fibula is the outer smaller bone of the lower leg. Its head is attached below the knee joint and its lower end is therefore lower than the end of the tibia, which explains the fact of the inner ankle being higher than the outer.

The bones of the foot

The root of the foot or tarsus owes its flexibility to the combination of seven closely fitting little bones called: astragalus, scaphoid, cuboid, 1st, 2nd and 3rd cuneiform and os calcis or heel bone. Then follow the five metatarsi or bones of the middle foot and finally the three phalanges of the four small toes and the two phalanges of the great toe; there is also the sesamoid bone below the base of the first metatarsal.

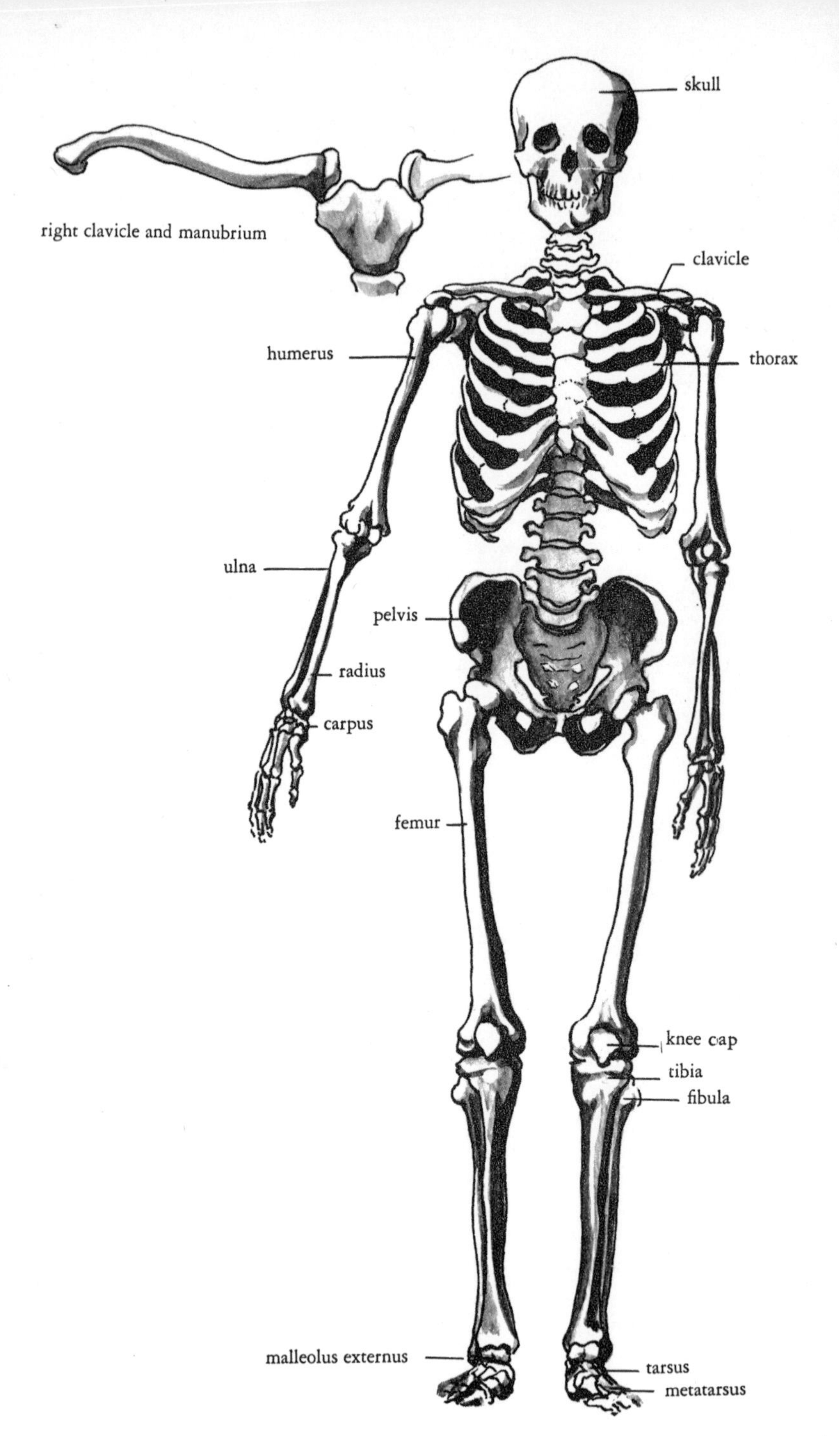
skull
right clavicle and manubrium
clavicle
humerus
thorax
ulna
pelvis
radius
carpus
femur
knee cap
tibia
fibula
malleolus externus
tarsus
metatarsus

SKELETON, FRONT

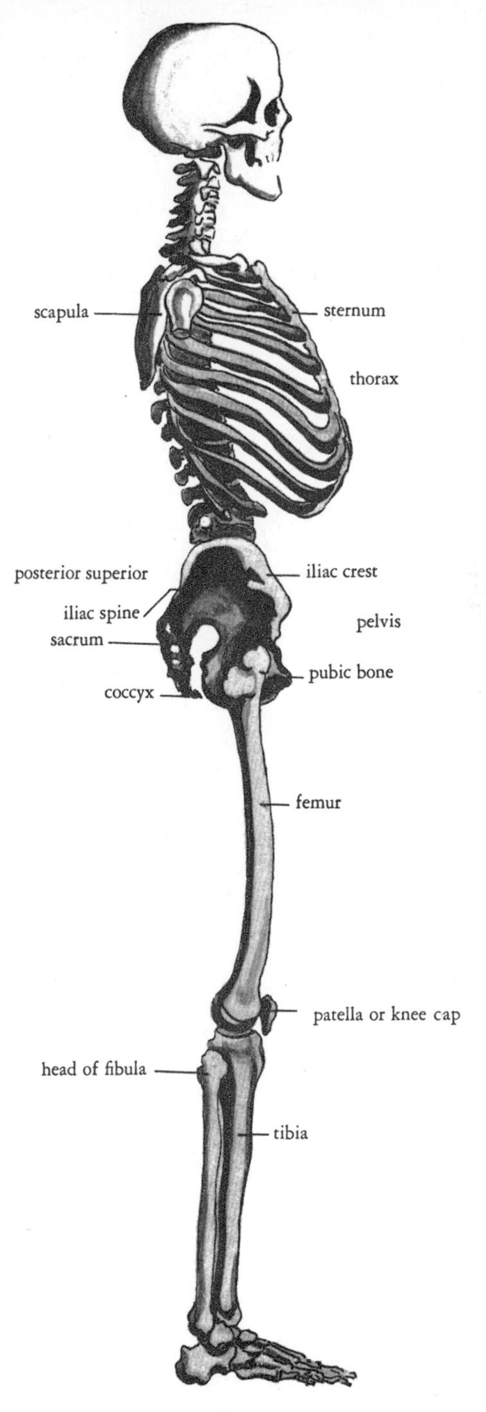
scapula
sternum
thorax
posterior superior
iliac spine
sacrum
coccyx
iliac crest
pelvis
pubic bone
femur
patella or knee cap
head of fibula
tibia

SKELETON PROFILE

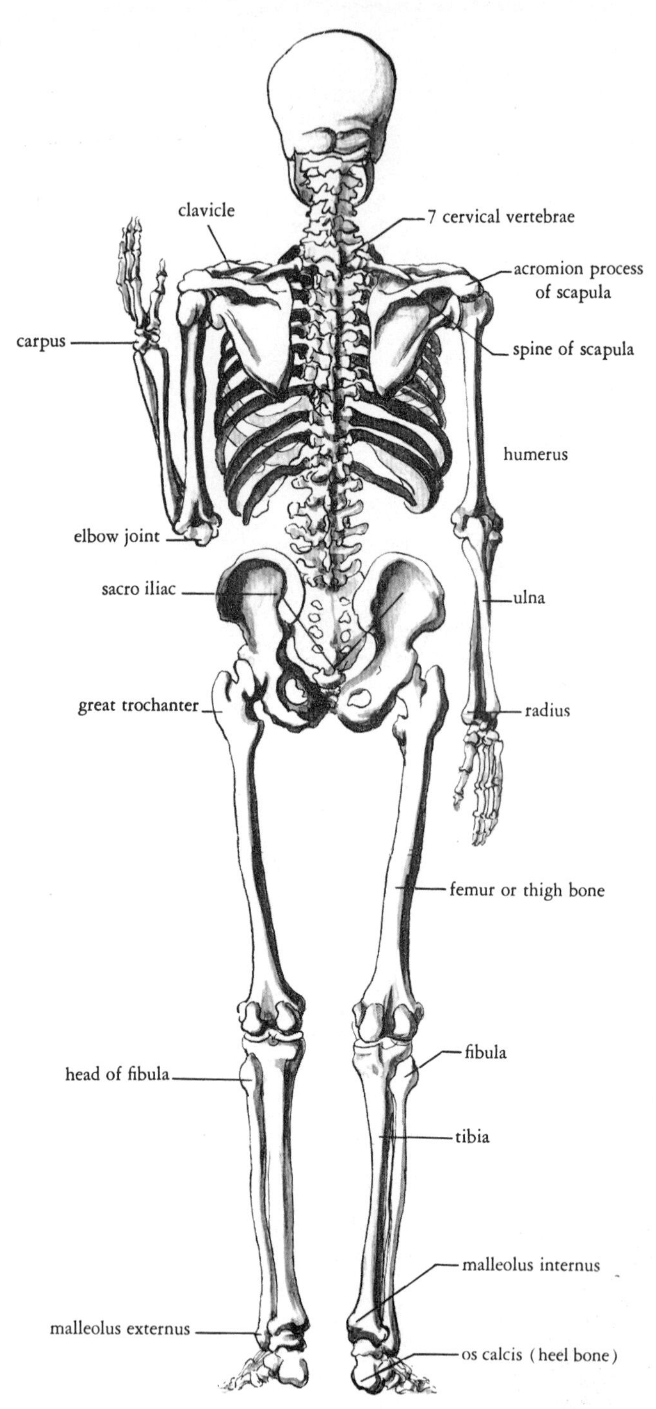
clavicle
7 cervical vertebrae
acromion process
of scapula
carpus
spine of scapula
humerus
elbow joint
sacro iliac
ulna
great trochanter
radius
femur or thigh bone
fibula
head of fibula
tibia
malleolus internus
malleolus externus
os calcis (heel bone)

Skeleton, Back View

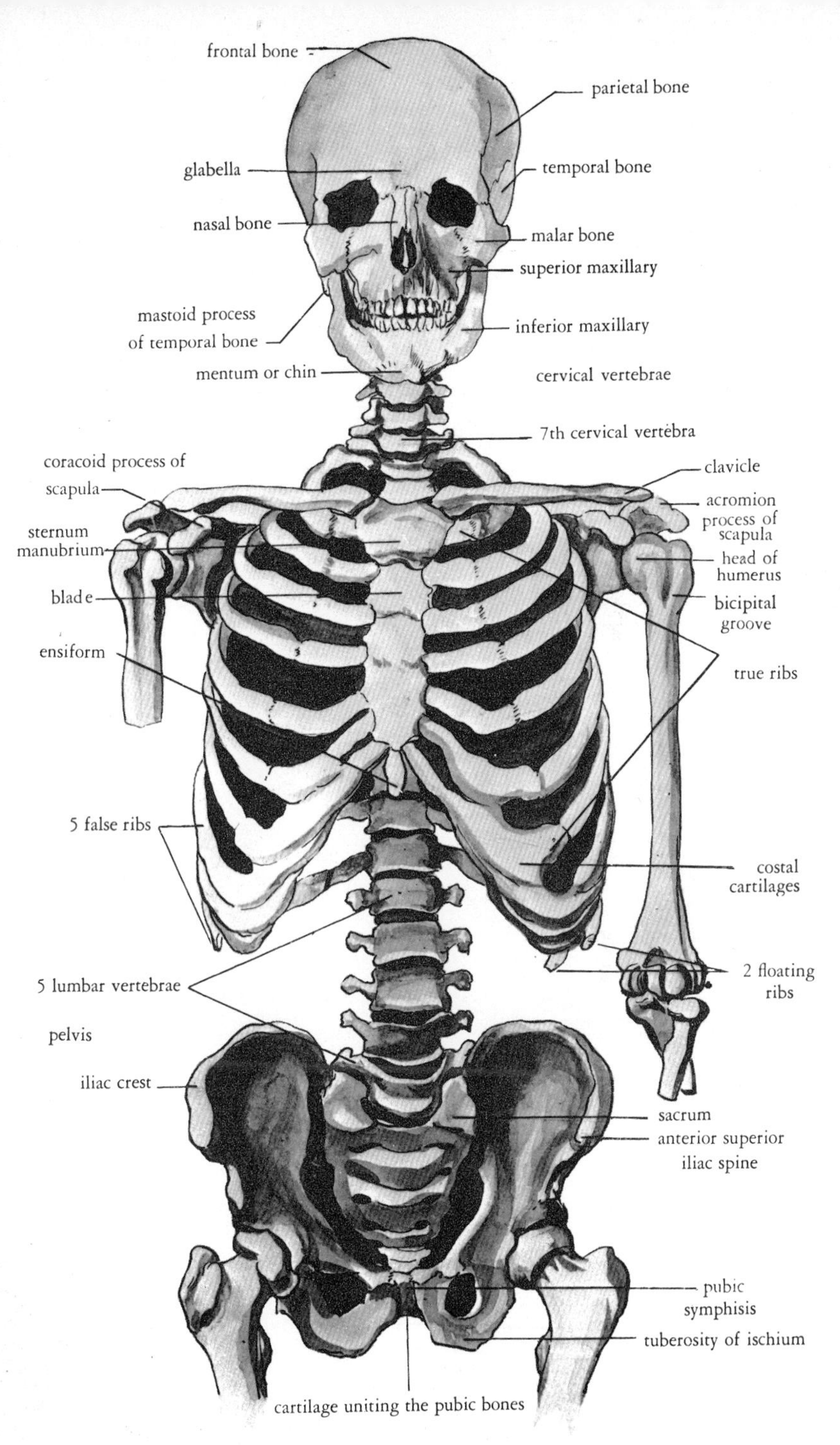
frontal bone
parietal bone
glabella
temporal bone
nasal bone
malar bone
superior maxillary
mastoid process
of temporal bone
inferior maxillary
mentum or chin
cervical vertebrae
7th cervical vertebra
coracoid process of
scapula
clavicle
acromion
process of
scapula
sternum
manubrium
head of
humerus
blade
bicipital
groove
ensiform
true ribs
5 false ribs
costal
cartilages
2 floating
ribs
5 lumbar vertebrae
pelvis
iliac crest
sacrum
anterior superior
iliac spine
pubic
symphisis
tuberosity of ischium
cartilage uniting the pubic bones

FRONT VIEW OF TRUNK (SKELETON)

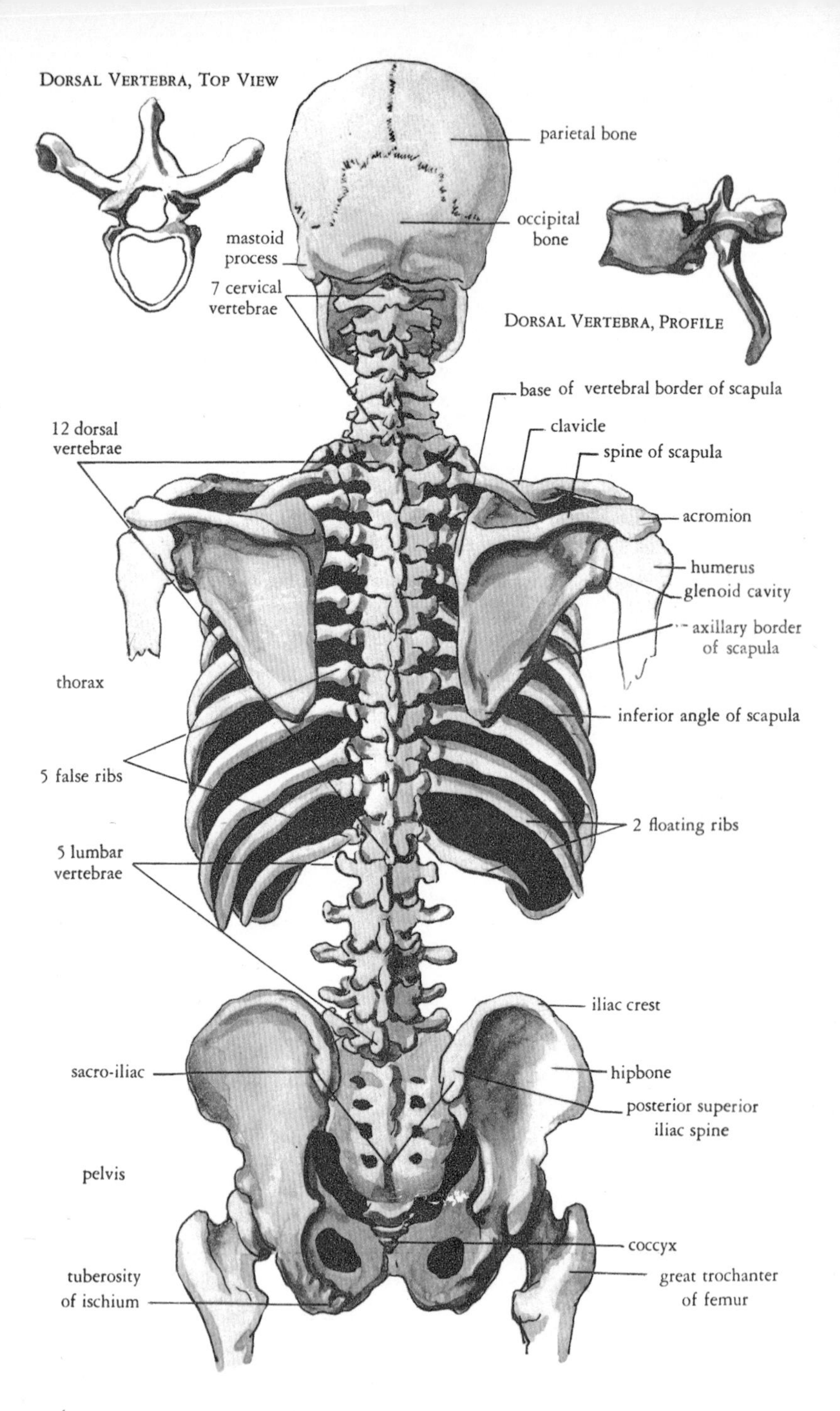

Dorsal Vertebra, Top View
parietal bone
occipital
bone
mastoid
process
7 cervical
vertebrae
Dorsal Vertebra, Profile
base of vertebral border of scapula
12 dorsal
vertebrae
clavicle
spine of scapula
acromion
humerus
glenoid cavity
axillary border
of scapula
thorax
inferior angle of scapula
5 false ribs
2 floating ribs
5 lumbar
vertebrae
iliac crest
sacro-iliac
hipbone
posterior superior
iliac spine
pelvis
coccyx
tuberosity
of ischium
great trochanter
of femur

Back View of Trunk (Skeleton)

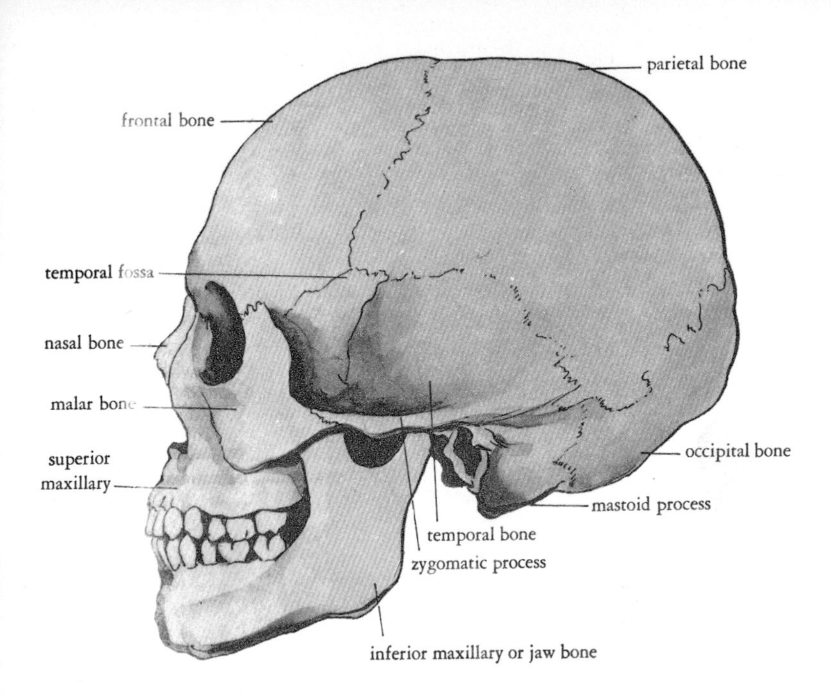
parietal bone
frontal bone
temporal fossa
nasal bone
malar bone
superior
maxillary
occipital bone
mastoid process
temporal bone
zygomatic process
inferior maxillary or jaw bone

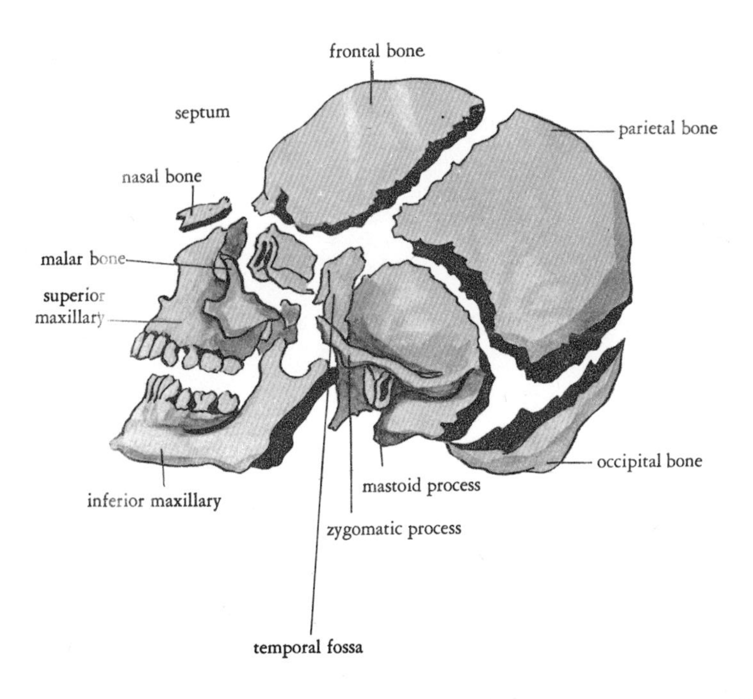
frontal bone
septum
parietal bone
nasal bone
malar bone
superior
maxillary
occipital bone
inferior maxillary
mastoid process
zygomatic process
temporal fossa

SKULL, PROFILE AND EXPLODED VIEW

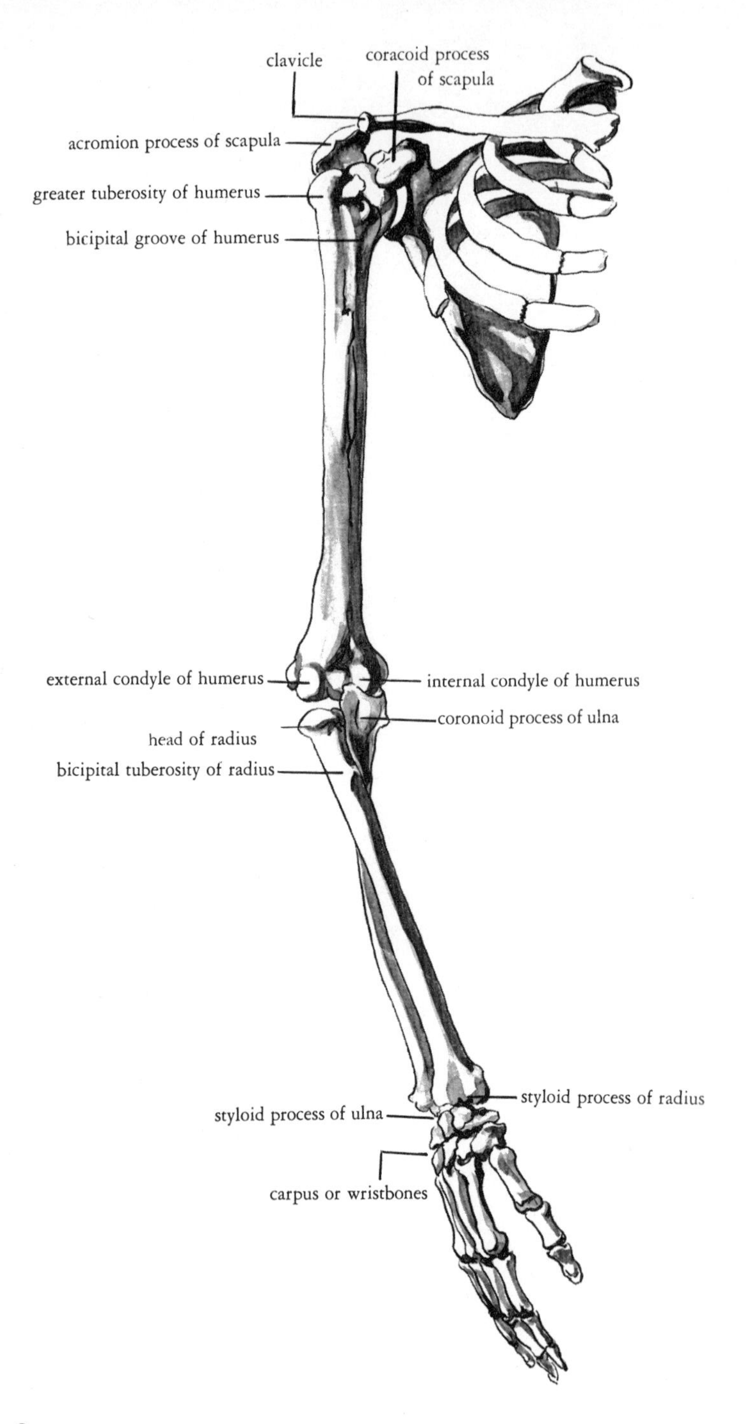
clavicle
coracoid process of scapula
acromion process of scapula
greater tuberosity of humerus
bicipital groove of humerus
external condyle of humerus
internal condyle of humerus
coronoid process of ulna
head of radius
bicipital tuberosity of radius
styloid process of radius
styloid process of ulna
carpus or wristbones

Front View of the Arm

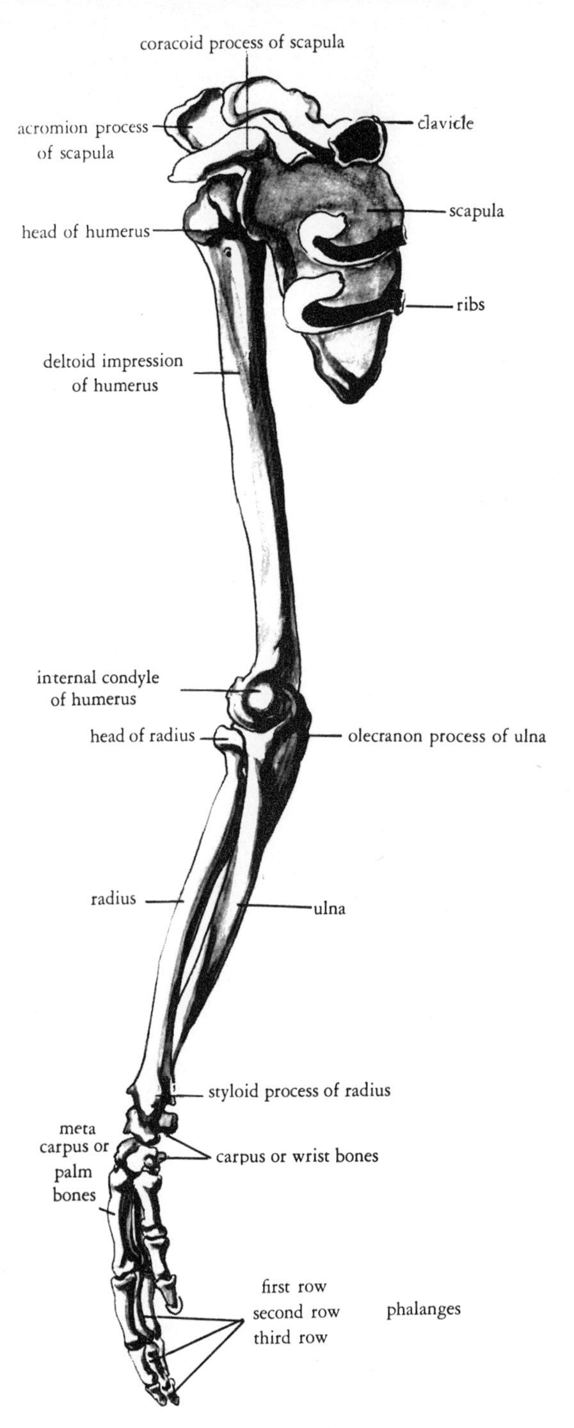
coracoid process of scapula
acromion process of scapula
clavicle
scapula
head of humerus
ribs
deltoid impression of humerus
internal condyle of humerus
head of radius
olecranon process of ulna
radius
ulna
styloid process of radius
meta carpus or palm bones
carpus or wrist bones
first row
second row
third row
phalanges

INNER VIEW OF RIGHT ARM

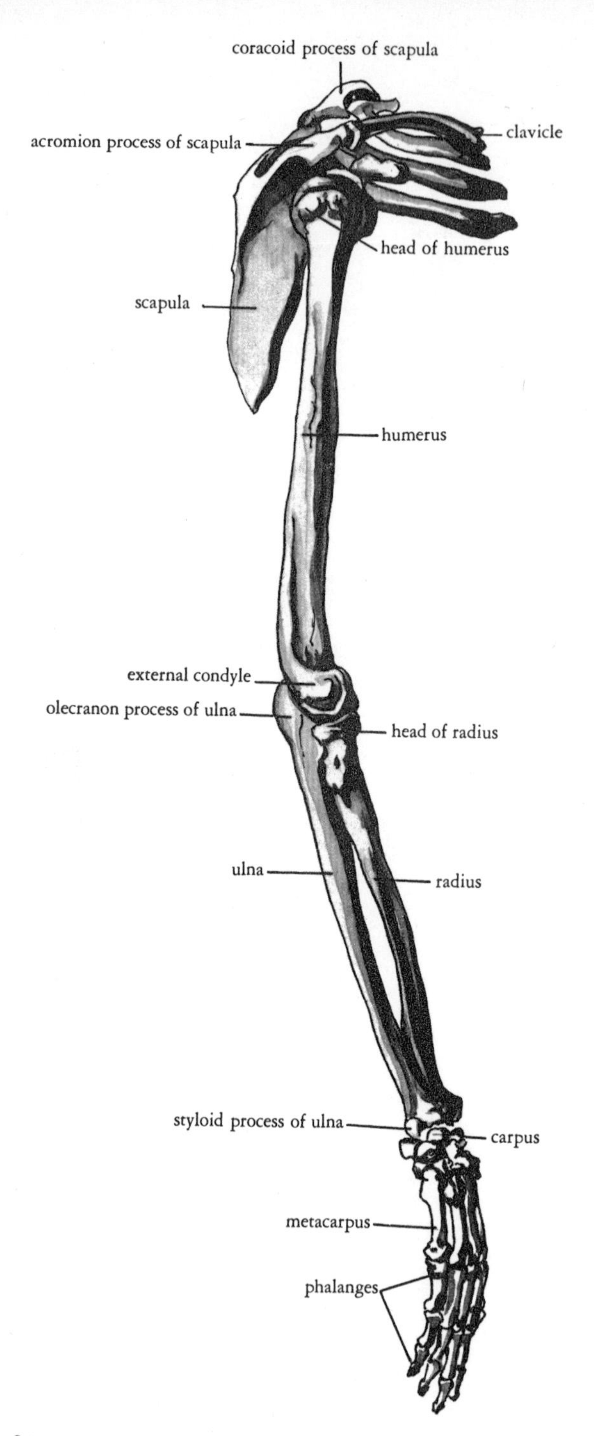
coracoid process of scapula
clavicle
acromion process of scapula
head of humerus
scapula
humerus
external condyle
olecranon process of ulna
head of radius
ulna
radius
styloid process of ulna
carpus
metacarpus
phalanges

OUTER VIEW OF THE RIGHT ARM

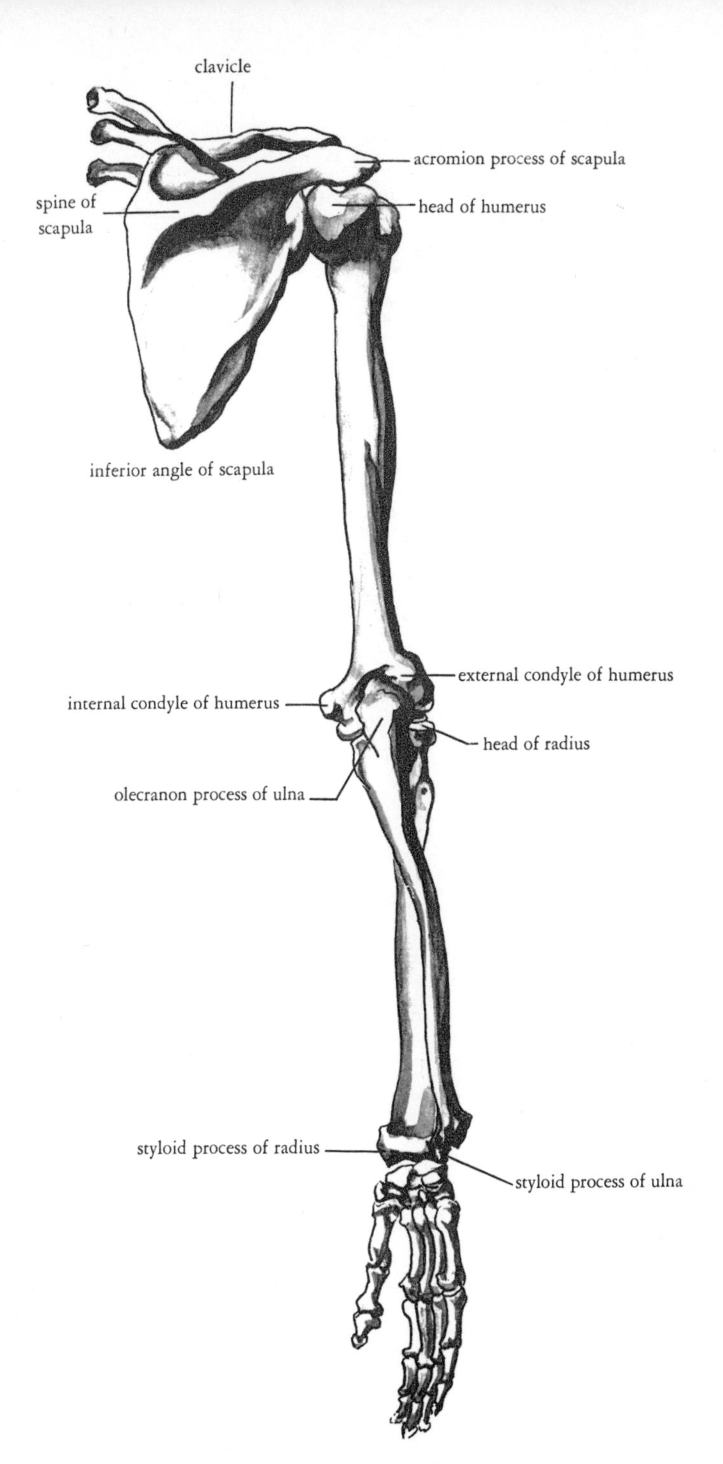
clavicle
acromion process of scapula
spine of scapula
head of humerus
inferior angle of scapula
external condyle of humerus
internal condyle of humerus
head of radius
olecranon process of ulna
styloid process of radius
styloid process of ulna

BACKVIEW OF RIGHT ARM

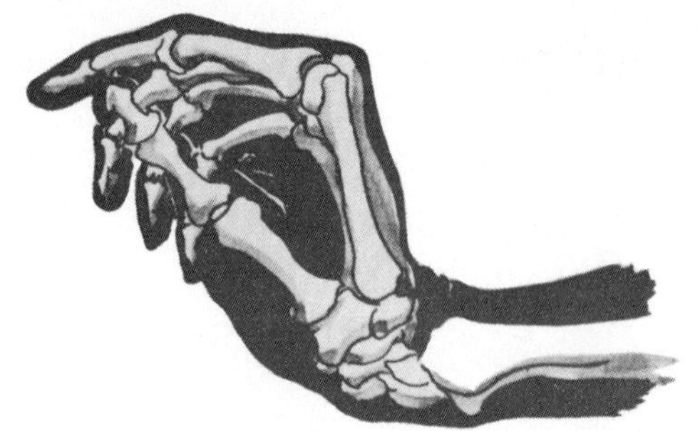

Movements of the Wrist (after Dr. J. Kollmann, 1910)

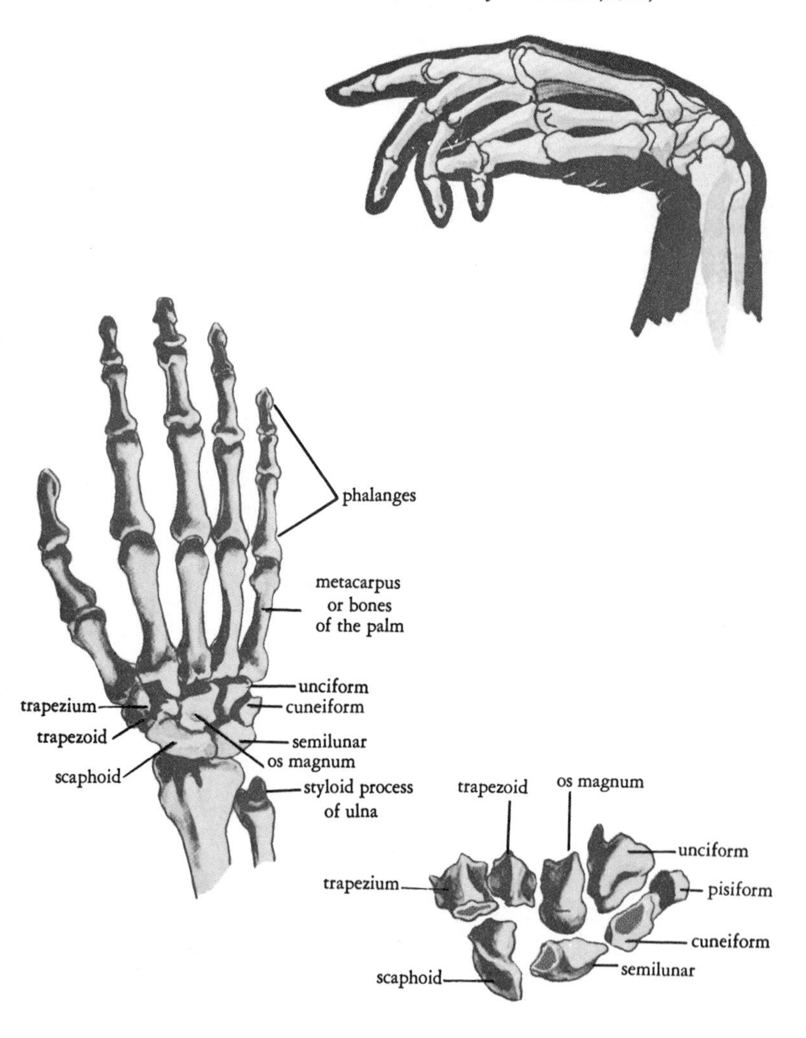
phalanges
metacarpus
or bones
of the palm
unciform
trapezium
cuneiform
trapezoid
semilunar
os magnum
scaphoid
styloid process
of ulna
trapezoid
os magnum
unciform
trapezium
pisiform
cuneiform
semilunar
scaphoid

Carpus or Wrist Bones, Exploded View

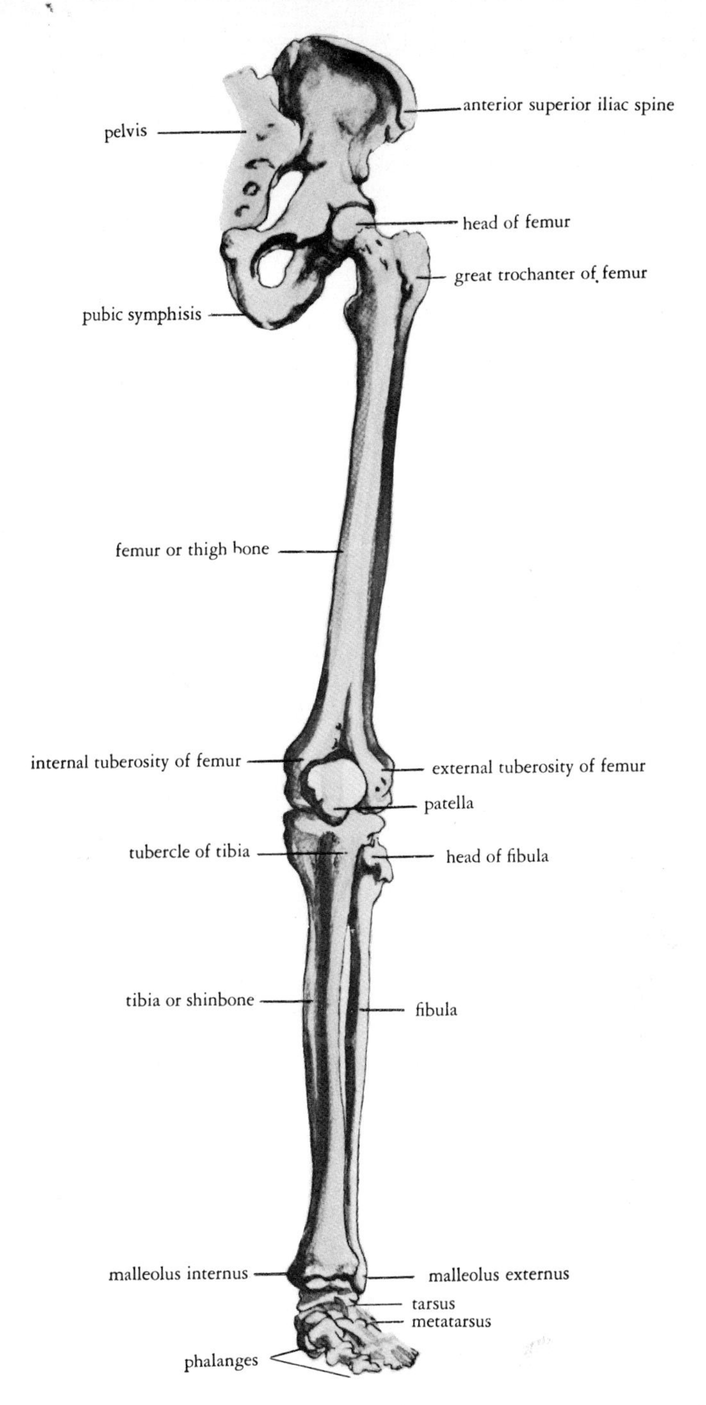
anterior superior iliac spine
pelvis
head of femur
great trochanter of femur
pubic symphisis
femur or thigh bone
internal tuberosity of femur
external tuberosity of femur
patella
tubercle of tibia
head of fibula
tibia or shinbone
fibula
malleolus internus
malleolus externus
tarsus
metatarsus
phalanges

Front View of Leg

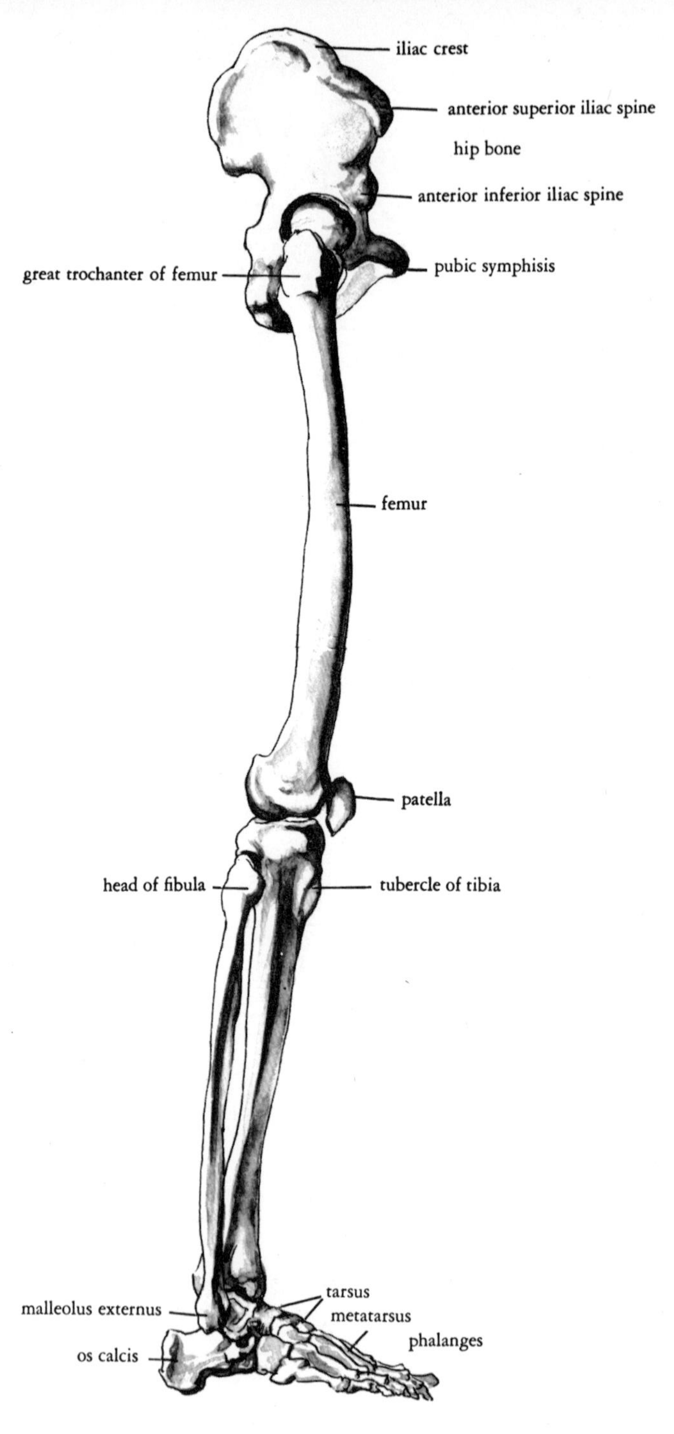
iliac crest
anterior superior iliac spine
hip bone
anterior inferior iliac spine
great trochanter of femur
pubic symphisis
femur
patella
head of fibula
tubercle of tibia
tarsus
malleolus externus
metatarsus
phalanges
os calcis

OUTER VIEW OF LEG

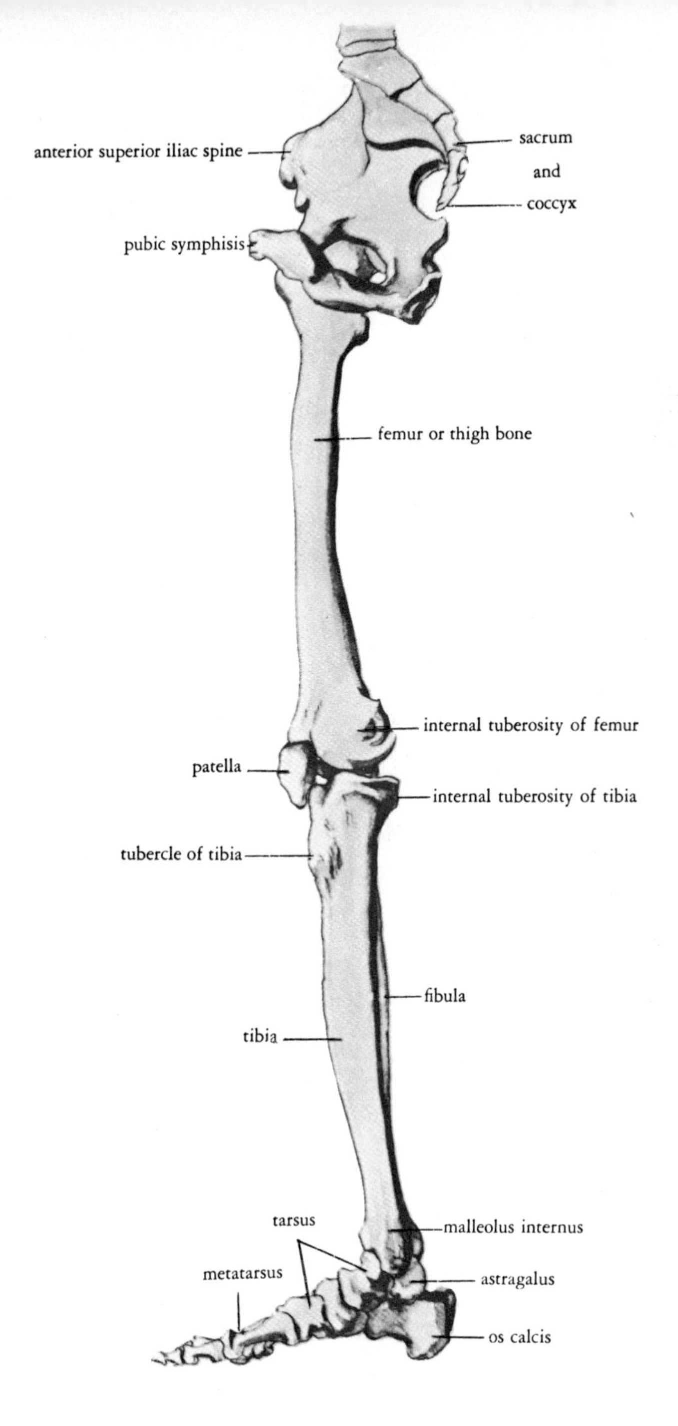
anterior superior iliac spine
sacrum
and
coccyx
pubic symphisis
femur or thigh bone
internal tuberosity of femur
patella
internal tuberosity of tibia
tubercle of tibia
fibula
tibia
tarsus
malleolus internus
metatarsus
astragalus
os calcis

Inner View of Leg

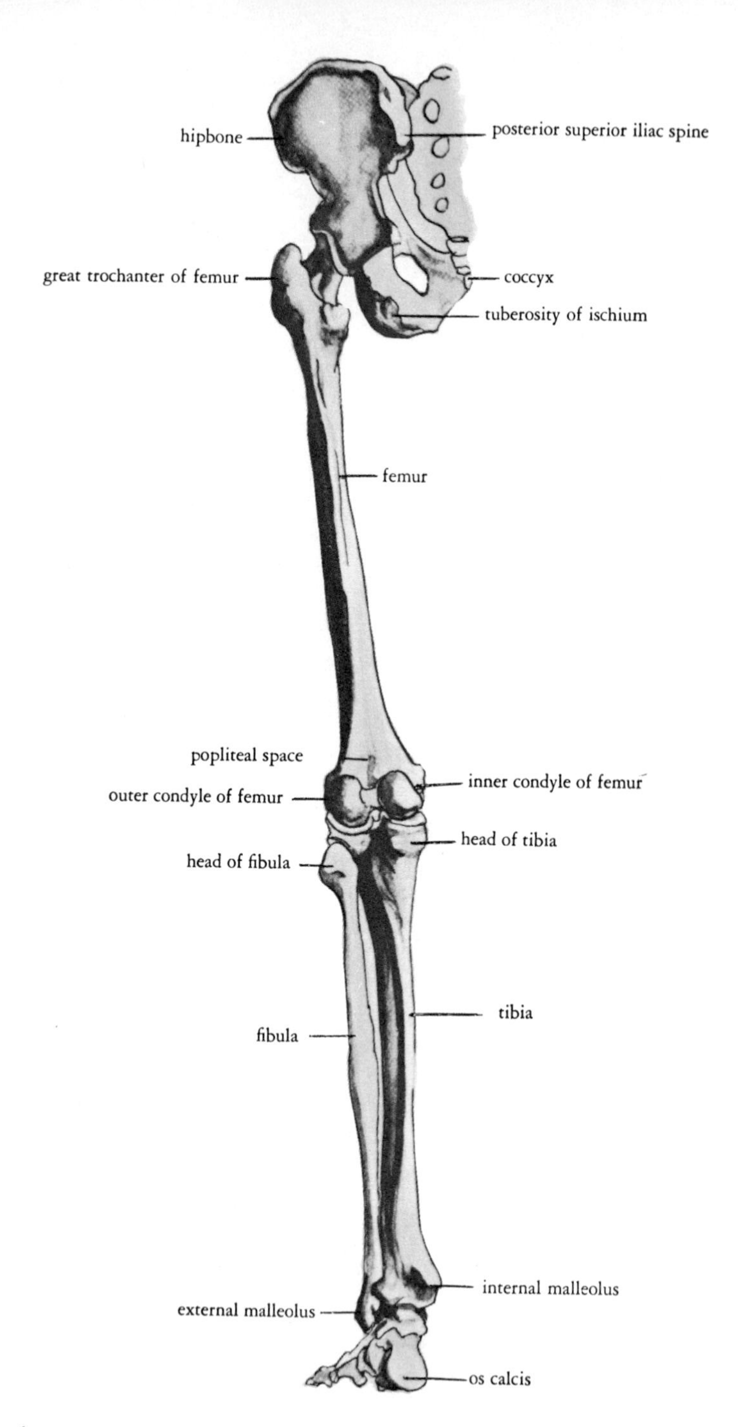
hipbone
posterior superior iliac spine
great trochanter of femur
coccyx
tuberosity of ischium
femur
popliteal space
inner condyle of femur
outer condyle of femur
head of tibia
head of fibula
tibia
fibula
internal malleolus
external malleolus
os calcis

BACK VIEW OF LEG

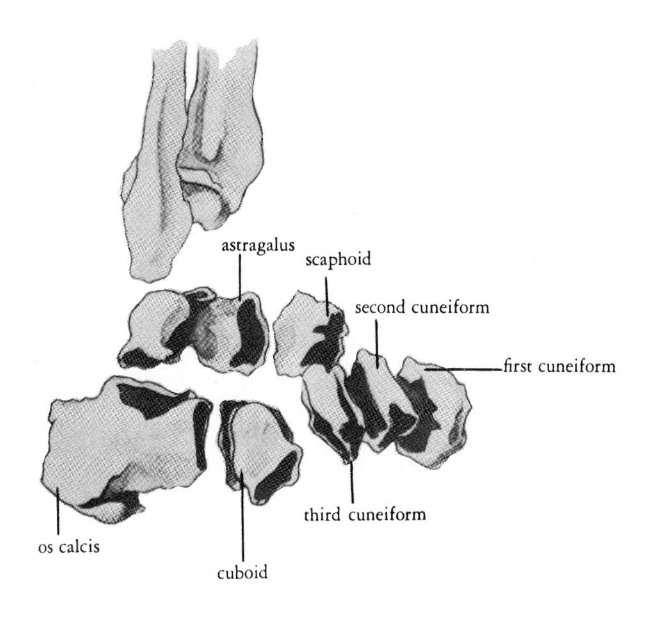
astragalus
scaphoid
second cuneiform
first cuneiform
third cuneiform
os calcis
cuboid

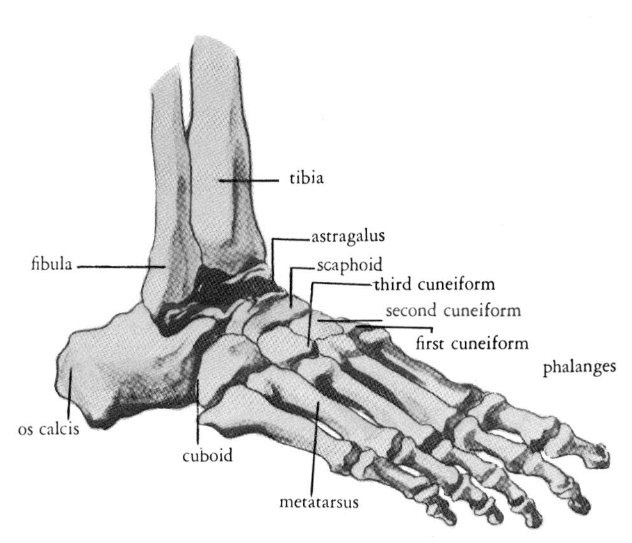
tibia
astragalus
fibula
scaphoid
third cuneiform
second cuneiform
first cuneiform
phalanges
os calcis
cuboid
metatarsus

TARSUS, OR ROOT OF THE FOOT, EXPLODED VIEW

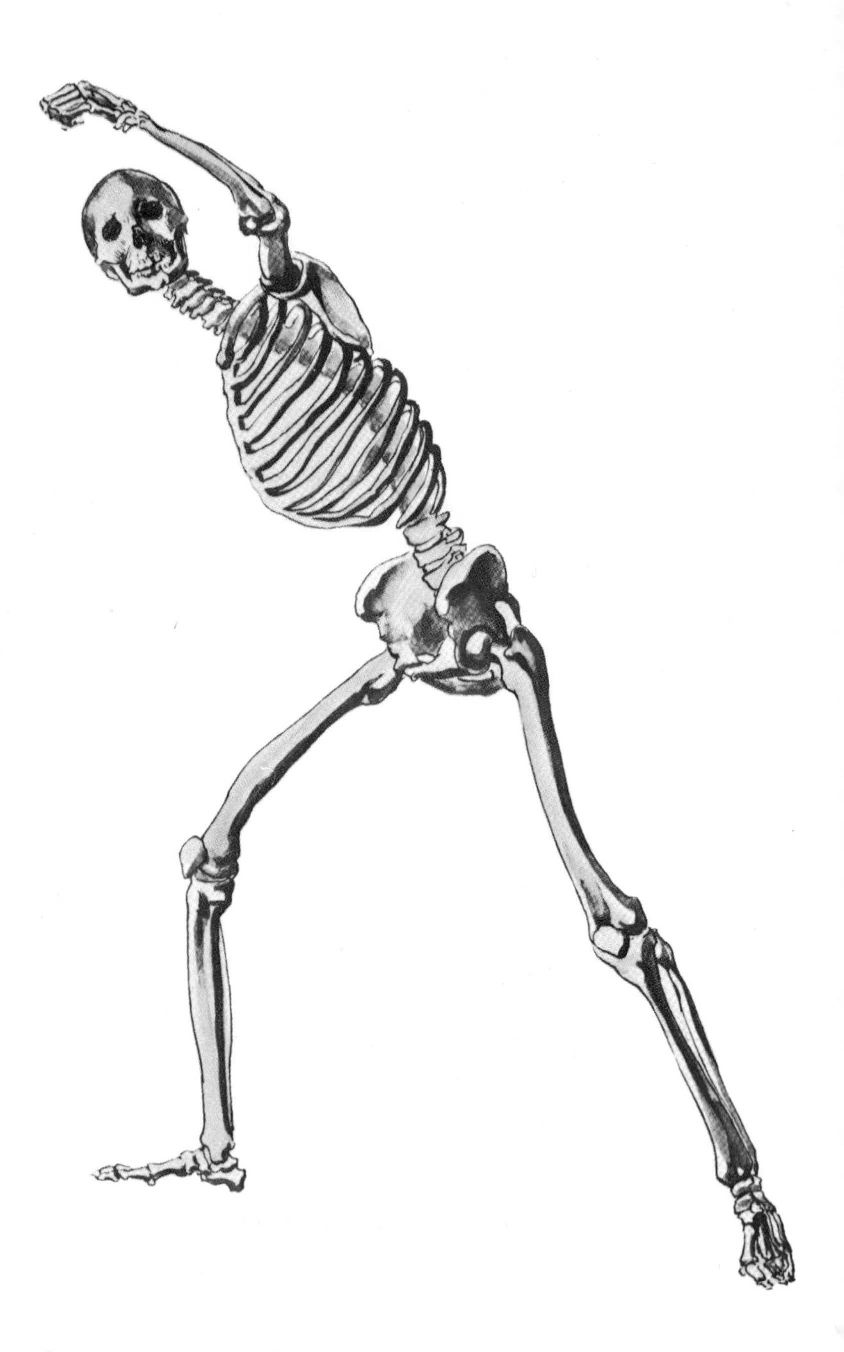

CHAPTER II

MUSCLES

The muscles of the head

The orbicularis palpebrarum closes the eyelid. It is attached to the frontal bone and the superior maxillary and it blends with the occipito frontalis.

The corrugator supercilii lifts the eyebrows and wrinkles the forehead into frowns. It is attached to the frontal bone at the internal angular process and to the occipito frontalis.

The pyramidalis nasi wrinkles the skin of the nose and enlarges the nostrils. It is attached to the occipito frontalis and disappears into the nasal bone.

The levator labii superioris lifts the wing of the nose and the upper lip. It is attached to the superior maxillary, tô the cartilage of the nose and to the upper lip.

The levator anguli oris lifts the corners of the mouth. It is attached to the superior maxillary and to the muscle at the corners of the mouth.

Zygomaticus major and minor lift and draw out the corners of the mouth. They are attached to the malarbone and to the corners of the mouth.

The buccinator closes the mouth and is attached to the superior and inferior maxillary bones and to the corners of the mouth.

The depressor anguli oris and *depressor labii inferioris* enlarge the mouth. They are attached to the inferior maxillary, to the corner of the mouth and to the lower lip.

The levator menti lifts the chin and is attached to the inferior maxillary and to the edge of the lower chin wall.

The muscles of the neck

The digastricus draws the lower jaw bone down. It is combined of two fleshy heads, which are united by a rounded tendon. The tendon is connected with the hyoid bone by a fibrous loop. The posterior head or belly is connected with the mastoid process of the temporal bone; the anterior belly arises from the lower jaw bone.

The platisma myoides muscle is a thin muscular fibre; it stretches the skin of the neck. It is attached to the fascia of the deltoid and pectoral muscles. It blends with the muscles around the lower part of the mouth and the inner edge of the lower jaw bone. It is so thin that the form of the underlying muscles is visible.

The sterno mastoid consists of two parts or heads. If only one part is contracted, it turns the head; if both are contracted, the head is lifted upward. Its inner part is attached to the sternum and the outer part is connected with the inner edge of the clavicle. They are inserted into the mastoid process of the temporal bone and into the curved edge of the occipital bone.

The omohyoid draws the hyoid bone down and backward. It is attached to the upper border of the scapula and to the hyoid bone.

The sterno hyoid also draws the hyoid bone down. It is attached to the clavicle and sternum and to the hyoid bone.

THE MUSCLES OF THE TRUNK

The pectoralis major draws the upper arm toward the front part of the chest and twists it inward. It is attached to the clavicle and to the entire length of the sternum and also to the cartilages of the 2nd to the 6th ribs. It is inserted into the humerus at the outer lip of the bicipital groove.

The serratus magnus draws the scapula forward and presses it firmly toward the rib cage. It is attached to the upper 8 ribs and to the vertebral border of the scapula. This muscle lies between the scapula and the ribs.

The deltoid muscle lifts the arm and is attached to the spine and acromion process of the scapula, to the clavicle and to the humerus at its V-shaped deltoid impression.

The rectus abdominus squeezes and enlarges the cavity of the abdominus. It is connected with the cartilages of the 5th, 6th and 7th ribs and with the tip of the sternum. Its lower end is attached to the pelvis at the pubic crest.

The external oblique muscle has the same function as the rectus abdominus. It is attached above to the lower 8 ribs by 8 digitations. Its lower ends are attached to the iliac crest of the pelvis.

THE MUSCLES OF THE BACK

The trapezius draws the scapula backward and also lifts the arm in drawing the scapula upward. It is attached to the occipital bone, to the spinous processes of all cervical and dorsal vertebrae and to the spine of the scapula and the outer part of the clavicle.

The rhomboidus major and *minor* draw the scapula toward the spine. They are covered by the trapezius and arise from the 7th to the 5th dorsal vertebrae. They are inserted into the inner edge of the scapula.

The latissimus dorsi draws the upper arm down and backward and twists it in its joints. It arises from the spinous processes of the 7 lower dorsal vertebrae, the spines of the lower 5 lumbar vertebrae, from the upper 3 sacral vertebrae, the lower 3 or 4 ribs and the posterior part of the iliac crest. It is inserted into the humerus below the bicipital groove by a short tendon.

The erector spinae erects the vertebral column and stretches it. It arises from the sacro-iliac groove and from the spines of the lumbar vertebrae and sacrum to the iliac crest. This muscle divides into two parts at the height of the second floating rib. The outer part "sacro lumbalis" is inserted into the ribs. The inner part "longissimus dorsi" is inserted into the processes of the dorsal vertebrae.

The teres major and *minor* arise from the back of the scapula and are inserted into the humerus below its head. The tendon of the teres minor unites with the tendon of the *infra spinatus,* which also arises from the back of the scapula.

The levator scapulae lifts the scapula and it arises with its four heads from the transverse processes of the upper 4 cervical vertebrae and is inserted into the upper angle of the scapula.

THE MUSCLES OF THE HIP

The gluteus maximus stretches the thigh in its hip joint, lifts the thigh backward and spreads it outward. Its upper end is attached to the iliac crest, the sacrum and coccyx and to the sacro-sciatic ligament. The lower end is inserted partly into the back of the femur and partly into the fascia lata of the thigh.

The gluteus medius spreads the leg and stretches the thigh in its hip joint. It is partly covered by the gluteus maximus. Its upper end arises partly from the iliac crest and partly from the outer surface of the ilium. Its flattened tendon is attached to the great trochanter of the femur.

The tensor vaginae or fascia femoris pulls the leg inward. It is attached to the iliac crest, its lower end being inserted into the fascia lata.

The sartorius pulls the lower leg inward in a bent position. It is attached to the anterior superior iliac spine and to the upper part of the inner tibia surface.

The quadriceps extensor lifts the patella in stretching the lower leg. It consists of: the rectus femoris, vastus externus, vastus internus and the crureus.

The rectus femoris is attached by two tendons to the pelvis.

The vastus externus is attached to the femur at the great trochanter.

The vastus internus and the *crureus,* which are covered by the rectus femoris, are attached to the shaft of the femur. The tendons of these four muscles are inserted into the patella and are also attached to the tubercle of the tibia.

THE MUSCLES OF THE ARM

The supinator longus turns the palm upward and bends the arm. It is attached to the lower half of the humerus and to the styloid process of the radius by a flat tendon.

The extensor carpi radialis longior stretches the fingers and the palm of the hand. It is attached to the upper third of the forearm and to the metacarpal bone of the index-finger. *The extensor carpi radialis brevior* stretches the hand both ways. It is attached to the nodus lateralis of the humerus and to the metacarpal bone of the middle finger.

The extensor communis digitorum stretches all four fingers. It is attached to the nodus lateralis of the humerus and to the second and third phalanges of all fingers, except the thumb, by five tendons.

The extensor carpi ulnaris stretches the arm. It is attached to the nodus lateralis and the metacarpal bone of the little finger.

The flexor carpi radialis turns the hand towards the spokebone or radius. It is attached to the nodus medialis of the humerus and to the metacarpal bone of the index finger.

The pronator teres turns the palm down and out, away from the body. It is attached to the lower part of the ulna and to the middle of the outer surface of the radius.

The palmaris longus bends the forearm and the hand. It is attached to the nodus medialis and the palmar fascia.

The flexor carpi ulnaris has the same function as the palmaris longus. It is attached to the nodus medialis and the pisiform bone. The flexors of the fingers (flexor profundus digitorum, flexor sublimis digitorum and flexor longus pollicis) lie under the flexors of the wrist and bend the fingers.

THE MUSCLES OF THE UPPER ARM

The biceps muscle bends the lower arm and draws it toward the upper arm, while turning the radius and the hand outward. It is divided into two heads. The shorter inner head arises from the coracoid process of the scapula, the longer head from the shoulder joint on the upper edge of the scapula. The two heads join at the middle of the upper arm into a flattened tendon, which is inserted into the tuberosity of the radius.

The coraco brachialis lifts the arm. It is attached to the coracoid process of the scapula and to the humerus.

The brachialis anticus bends the forearm and stretches the elbow joint. It covers the lower half of the front part of the humerus. It is inserted into the coronoid process of the ulna by a thick tendon.

The triceps stretches the arm. It has three parts or heads, called: *the middle* or *long head, the external head, the internal* or *short head*. The middle head arises below the glenoid cavity of the scapula, the external head from the back of the humerus, and the short head equally from the back of the humerus. The tendon, which receives its fibres from these three heads, has a flattened form, which is distinctly visible at the surface of the upper arm. It is inserted into the olecranon process of the ulna.

THE MUSCLES OF THE HAND (THE PALM)

The flexor brevis pollicis bends the first phalanx of the thumb. It arises partly from the annular ligament and partly from the palm. It is inserted into the first phalanx of the thumb.

The abductor pollicis pulls the thumb down. It arises from the trapezium and the annular ligament and is inserted into the first phalanx.

The adductor obliquus pulls the thumb toward the hand. It is attached to the os magnum, the adductor transversus from the metacarpal bone of the middle finger and to the first phalanx.

Opponens pollicis pulls the thumb close to the four fingers and toward the palm. It is attached to the annular ligament, the trapezium bone and the metacarpal bone.

The abductor minimi draws the little finger outward. It is attached to the pisiform bone and to the first phalanx of the little finger.

The flexor brevis minimi digiti bends the little finger. It is attached to the unciform bone and the first phalanx of the little finger.

The opponens minimi digiti draws the little finger toward the thumb. It starts out from the annular ligament and is inserted into the metacarpal bone.

The four lumbricales are next to and are parallel to the tendons of the four fingers in the palm of the hand. They bend the four fingers at their first phalanges.

The interossei muscles close the hand. There are four dorsal and three palmar muscles between the metacarpal bones.

THE MUSCLES OF THE LEG AND FOOT

The adductor longus is attached to the pubic portion of the pelvis and is inserted into the back of the femur. It pulls the legs toward each other and crosses the legs as does the adductor brevis. The adductor magnus arises at the pubic bones and ischium and is inserted into the back of the femur and also into the tubercle on the inner condyle of the femur.

The iliacus and *psoas* arise from the pelvis at the iliac crest and from the vertebrae and are attached to the trochanter of the femur lifting the thigh.

The pectineus arises from the pelvis and is attached to the back of the femur.

The semitendinosus belongs to the backperiphery of the thigh and arises from the tuberosity of the ischium. It is inserted into the upper part of the tibia bending the lower leg toward the thigh.

The semimembranosus has the same function as the semitendinosus. It arises from the ischium and is attached to the inner tuberosity of the tibia.

The biceps bends the lower leg. It arises by two heads—the long head from the back of the tuberosity of the ischium, the short head from the back of the femur. It is inserted into the head of the fibula, with an expansion to the tibia.

The gastrocnemius lifts the os calcis. It is divided into two heads, one short and one long. It is attached to the femur above the condyle and its lower end forms the tendon achilles in joining with the soleus.

The soleus, which has the same function as the gastrocnemius is attached to the back of the tibia and fibula. It is a flat muscle, similar to the shape of the fish called the sole. The tibialis anticus lifts the front and inner edge of the foot. It is attached to the outer tuberosity of the tibia and to the cuneiform bone and metatarsal bone of the big toe.

The flexor longus digitorum bends and moves the four smaller toes by being attached to the flexor longus pollicis, which bends the big toe.

The extensor longus digitorum stretches the four smaller toes, is attached to the outer tuberosity of the tibia and, passing through the annular ligament, is also attached to the four outer toes at their 2nd and 3rd phalanges.

The extensor proprius pollicis moves and stretches the big toe. It is attached to the front of the fibula and to the last phalanx of the big toe.

The peroneus longus and *brevis* stretch the foot and lift its outer edge.

The peroneus longus is attached to the outer surface of the fibula and, by a very long tendon, to the lower part of the cuboid bone. From the cuboid bone it passes across the sole of the foot, to be connected with the cuneiform bone and the metatarsal bone of the great toe.

The peroneus brevis is attached to the fibula and to the 5th metatarsal bone.

The extensor brevis digitorum stretches the toes, is attached to the os calcis and divides into four tendons to the four inner toes. It is plainly visible in front of the external malleolus. The internal and external interossei spread the toes and pull them toward each other. The adductors and abductors of the toes are muscles of the sole of the foot and are too deep seated to have a noticeable influence on the outer form of the foot.

The abductor pollicis draws the big toe downward. It is connected with the os calcis and with the 1st phalanx of the big toe.

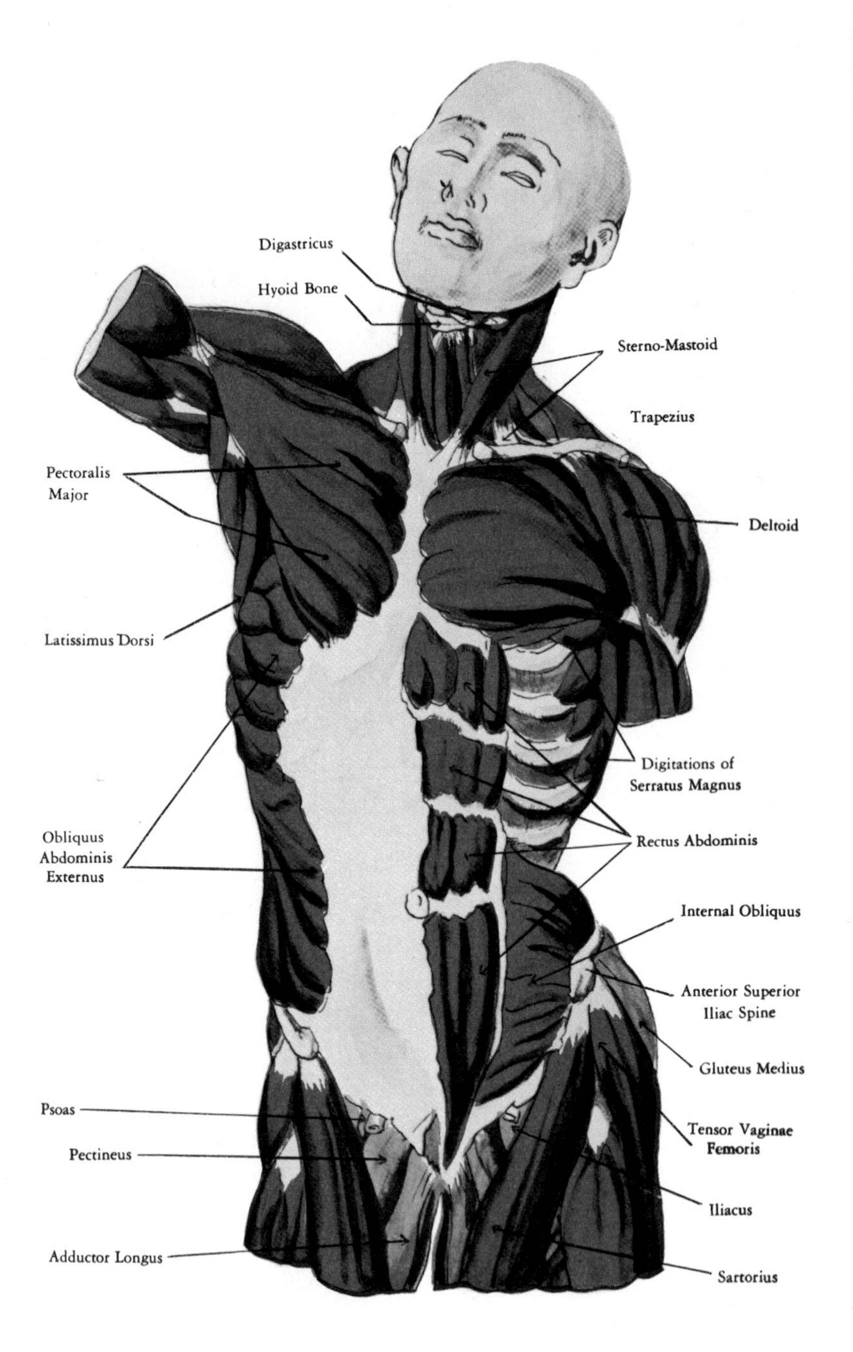
Digastricus
Hyoid Bone
Sterno-Mastoid
Trapezius
Pectoralis Major
Deltoid
Latissimus Dorsi
Digitations of Serratus Magnus
Obliquus Abdominis Externus
Rectus Abdominis
Internal Obliquus
Anterior Superior Iliac Spine
Gluteus Medius
Psoas
Tensor Vaginae Femoris
Pectineus
Iliacus
Adductor Longus
Sartorius

Front View of Trunk

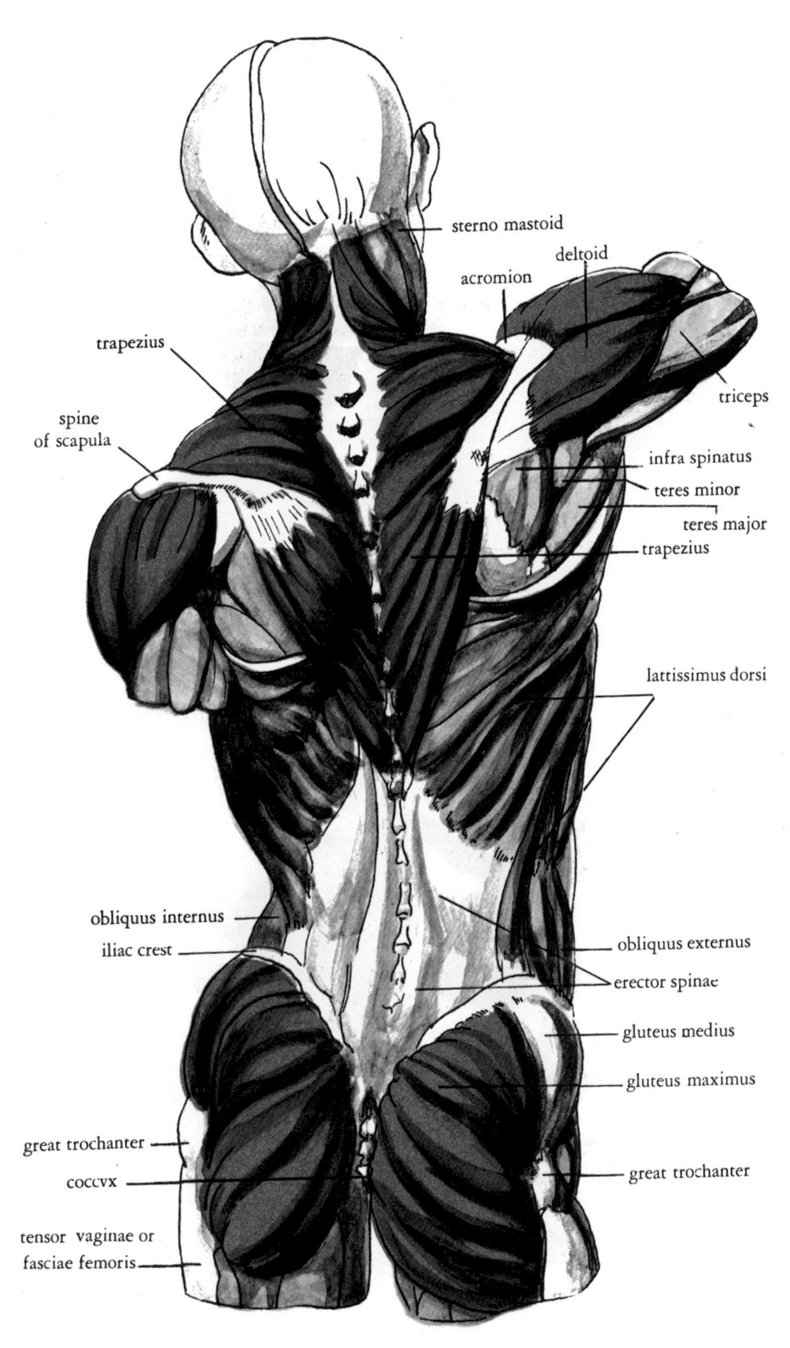
sterno mastoid
deltoid
acromion
trapezius
triceps
spine
of scapula
infra spinatus
teres minor
teres major
trapezius
lattissimus dorsi
obliquus internus
iliac crest
obliquus externus
erector spinae
gluteus medius
gluteus maximus
great trochanter
coccyx
great trochanter
tensor vaginae or
fasciae femoris

BACK VIEW OF TRUNK

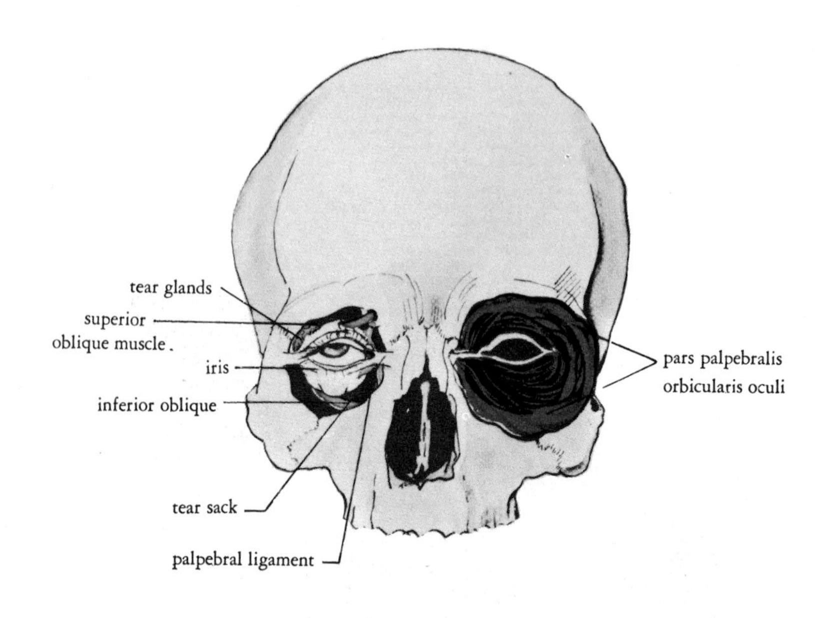
tear glands
superior
oblique muscle
iris
inferior oblique
tear sack
palpebral ligament
pars palpebralis
orbicularis oculi

Upper Part of Skull with Eyeball and Eye Muscle

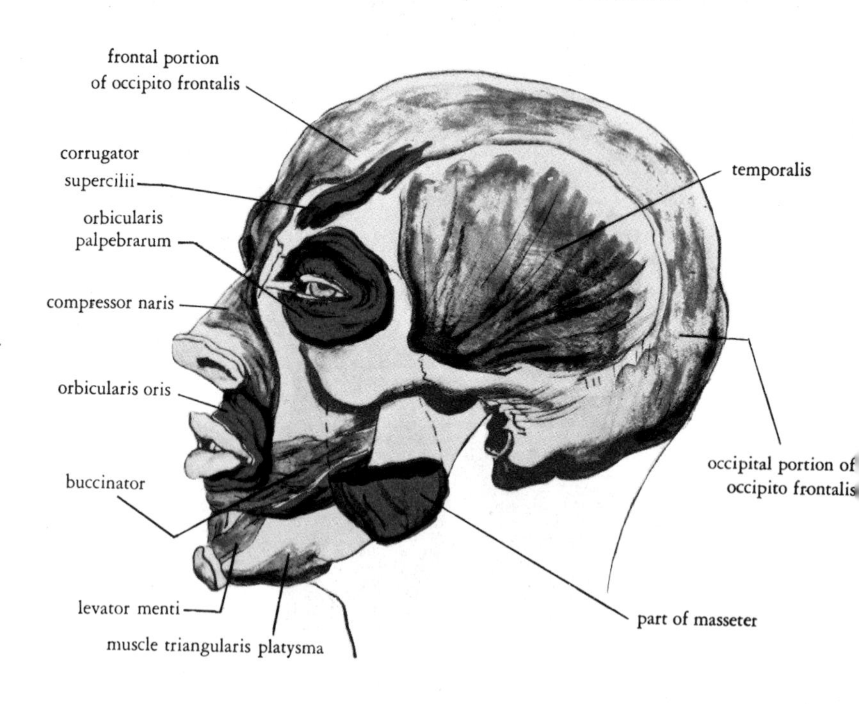
frontal portion
of occipito frontalis
corrugator
supercilii
orbicularis
palpebrarum
compressor naris
orbicularis oris
buccinator
levator menti
muscle triangularis platysma
temporalis
occipital portion of
occipito frontalis
part of masseter

Face Muscles, Profile

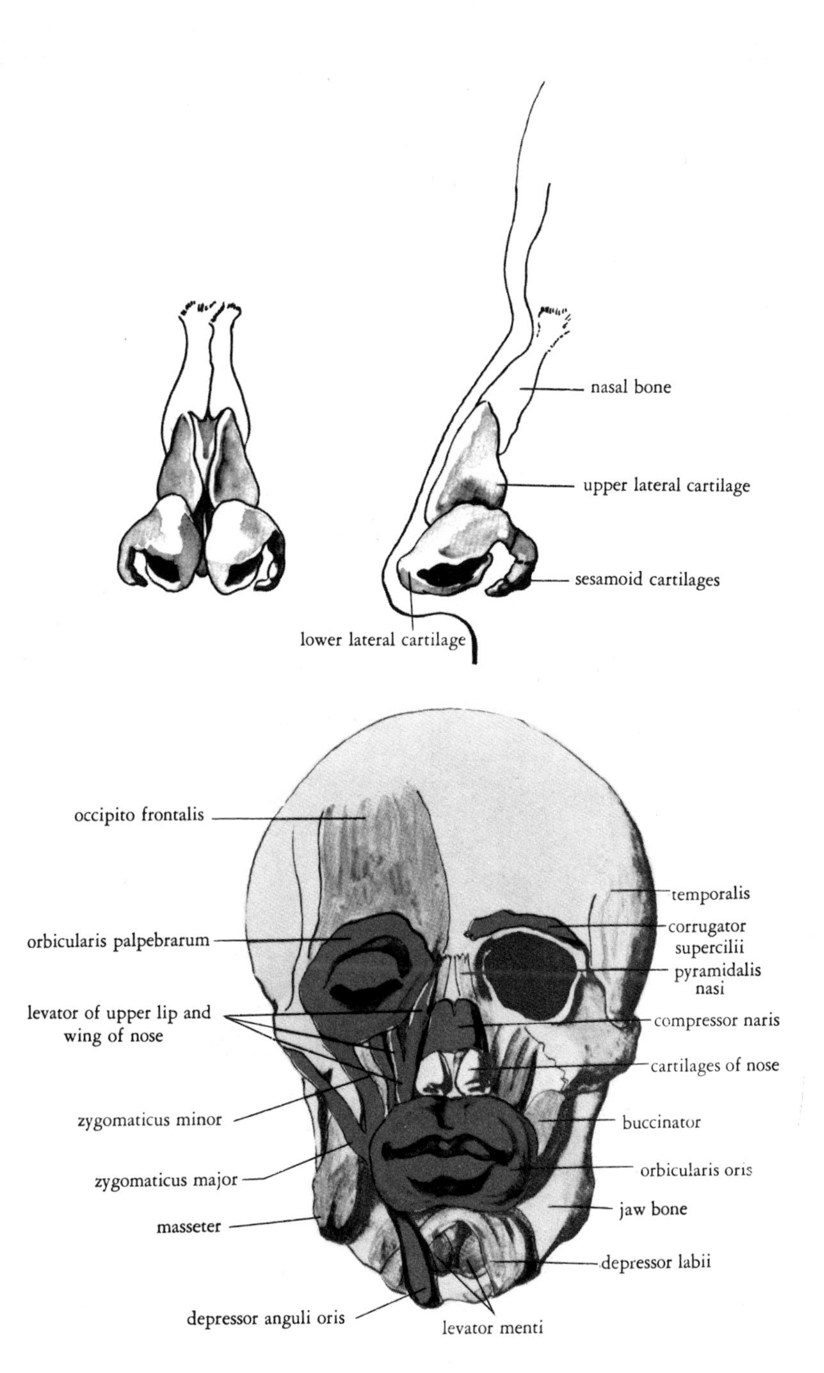
nasal bone
upper lateral cartilage
sesamoid cartilages
lower lateral cartilage
occipito frontalis
temporalis
corrugator
supercilii
orbicularis palpebrarum
pyramidalis
nasi
levator of upper lip and
wing of nose
compressor naris
cartilages of nose
zygomaticus minor
buccinator
orbicularis oris
zygomaticus major
jaw bone
masseter
depressor labii
depressor anguli oris
levator menti

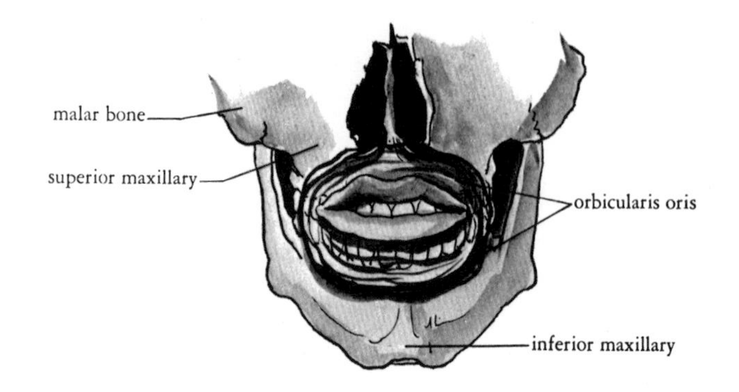
malar bone
superior maxillary
orbicularis oris
inferior maxillary

LOWER PART OF SKULL AND MUSCLE OF THE MOUTH

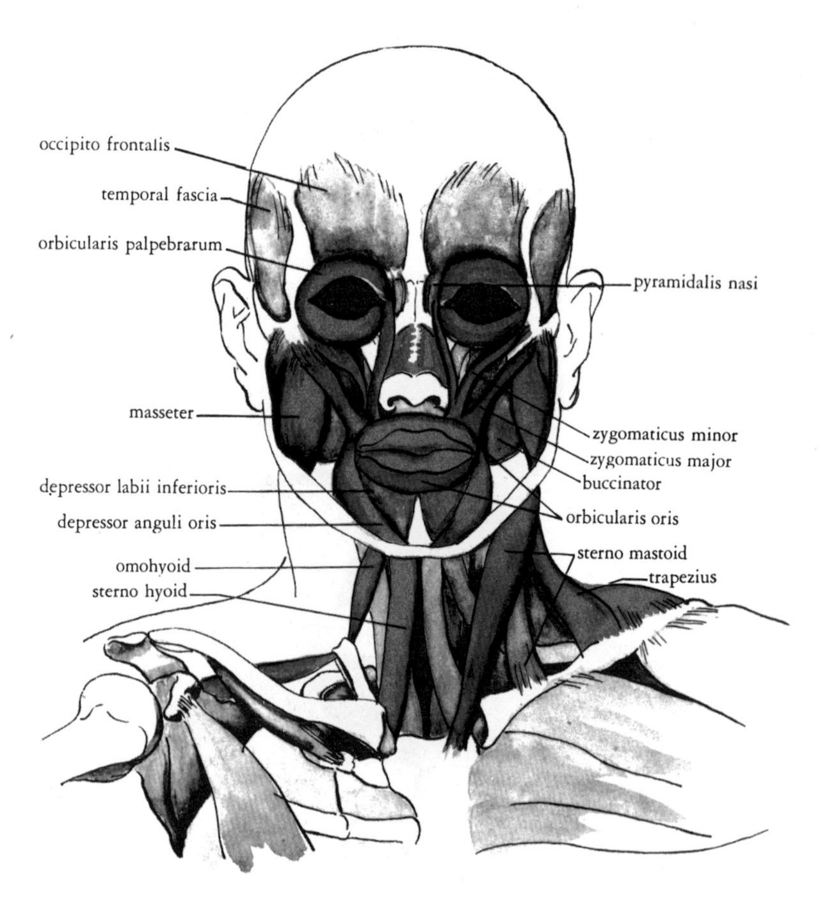
occipito frontalis
temporal fascia
orbicularis palpebrarum
pyramidalis nasi
masseter
zygomaticus minor
zygomaticus major
buccinator
depressor labii inferioris
depressor anguli oris
orbicularis oris
sterno mastoid
omohyoid
trapezius
sterno hyoid

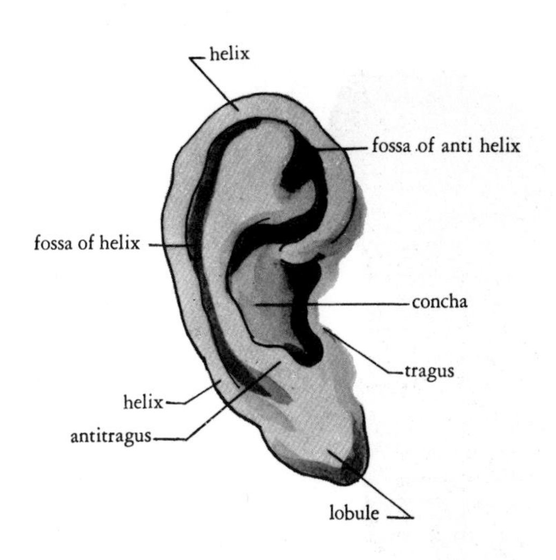
helix
fossa of anti helix
fossa of helix
concha
tragus
helix
antitragus
lobule

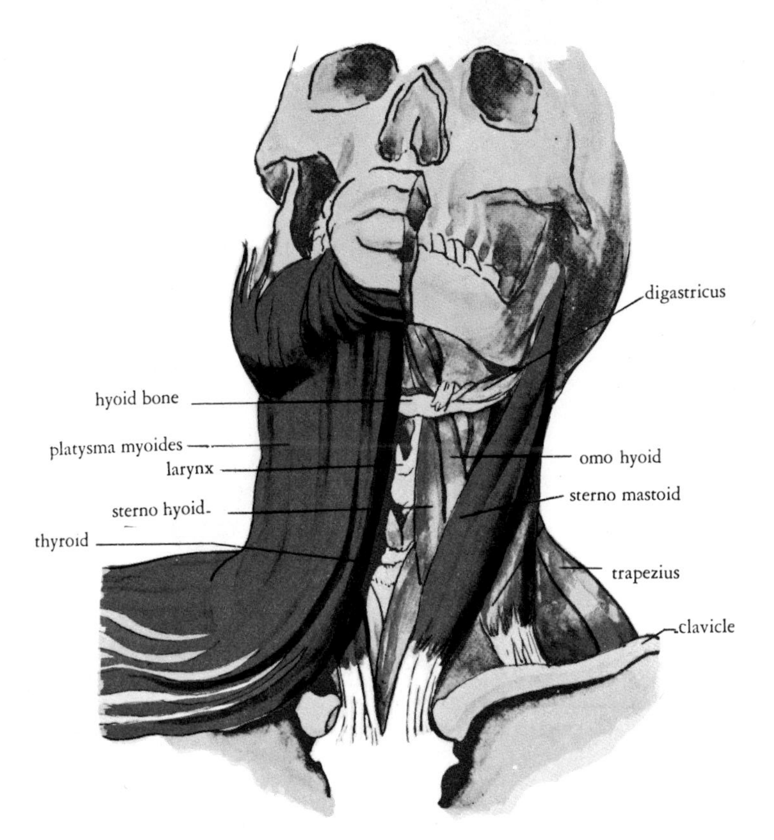
digastricus
hyoid bone
platysma myoides
omo hyoid
larynx
sterno mastoid
sterno hyoid
thyroid
trapezius
clavicle

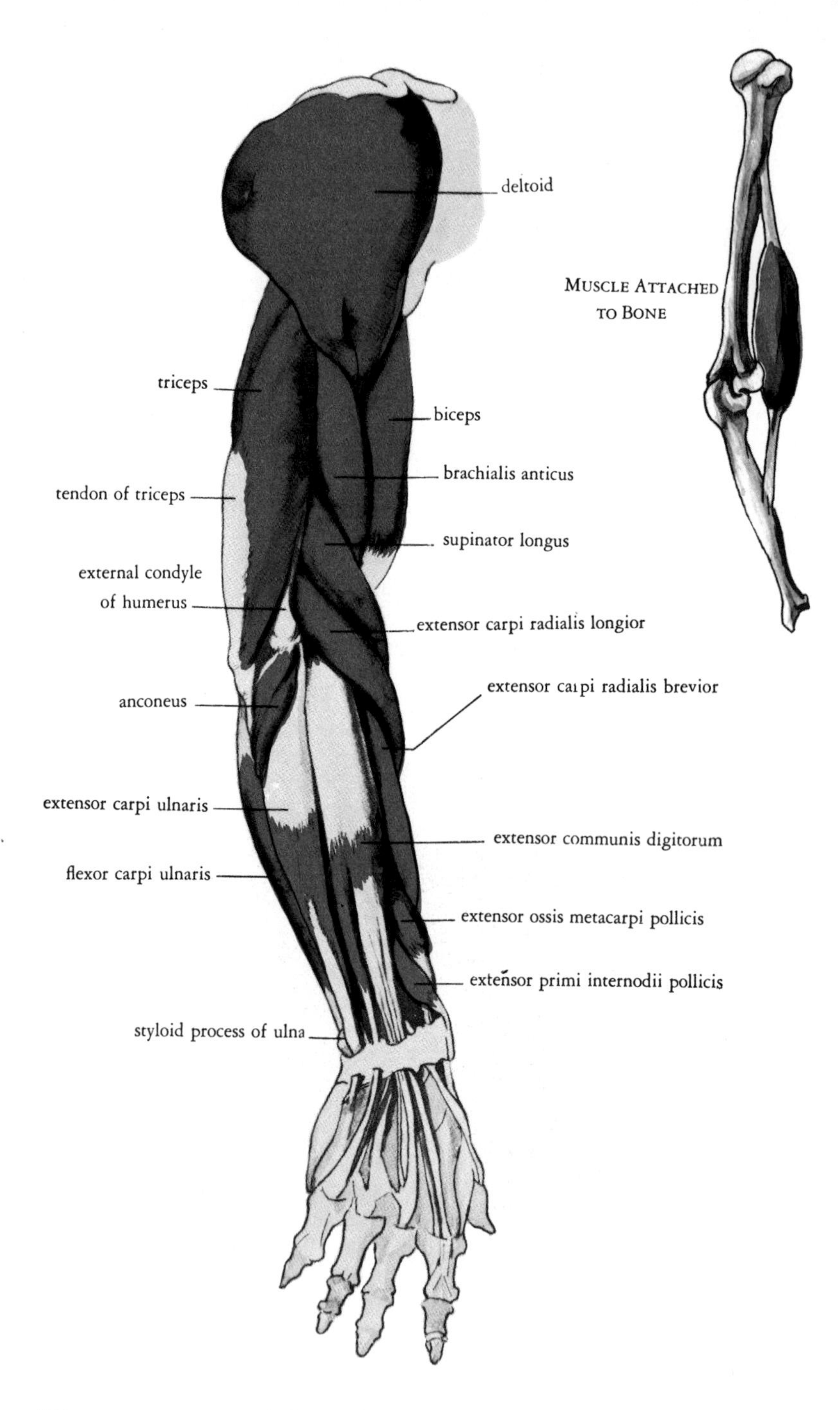
deltoid
Muscle Attached
to Bone
triceps
biceps
brachialis anticus
tendon of triceps
supinator longus
external condyle
of humerus
extensor carpi radialis longior
extensor carpi radialis brevior
anconeus
extensor carpi ulnaris
extensor communis digitorum
flexor carpi ulnaris
extensor ossis metacarpi pollicis
extensor primi internodii pollicis
styloid process of ulna

Stretched Arm, Outer View

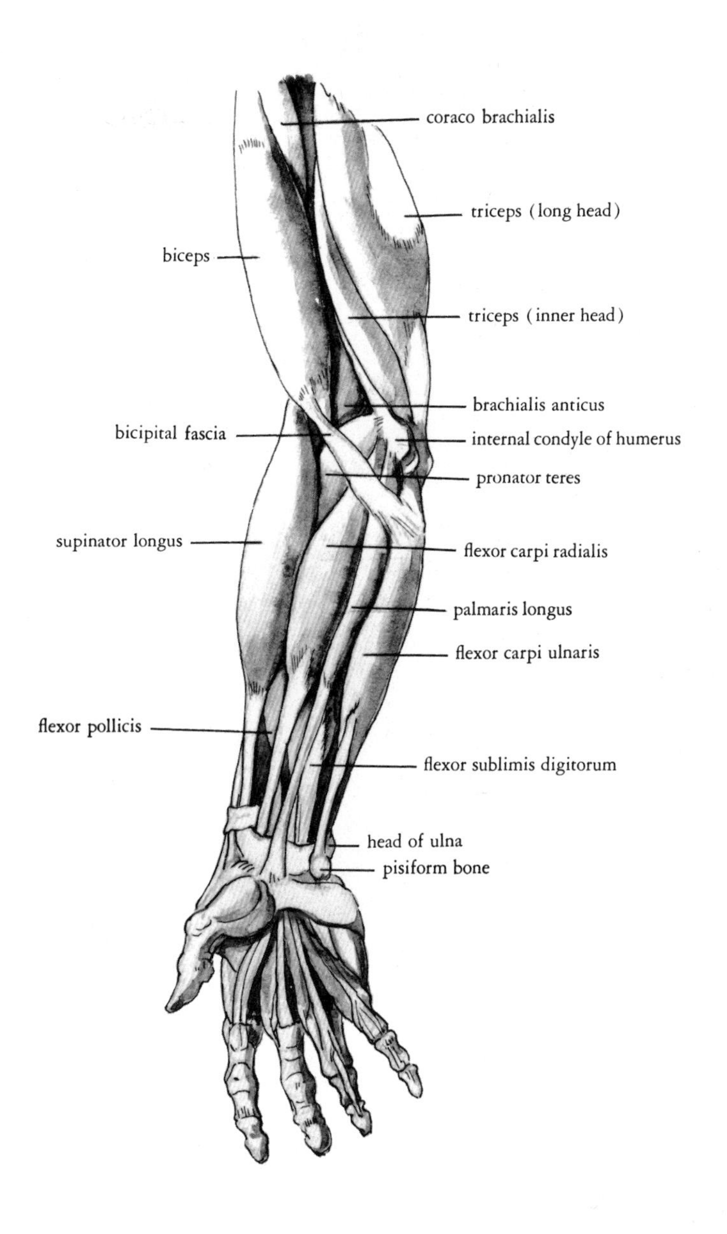
coraco brachialis
triceps (long head)
biceps
triceps (inner head)
brachialis anticus
bicipital fascia
internal condyle of humerus
pronator teres
supinator longus
flexor carpi radialis
palmaris longus
flexor carpi ulnaris
flexor pollicis
flexor sublimis digitorum
head of ulna
pisiform bone

STRETCHED ARM, INNER VIEW

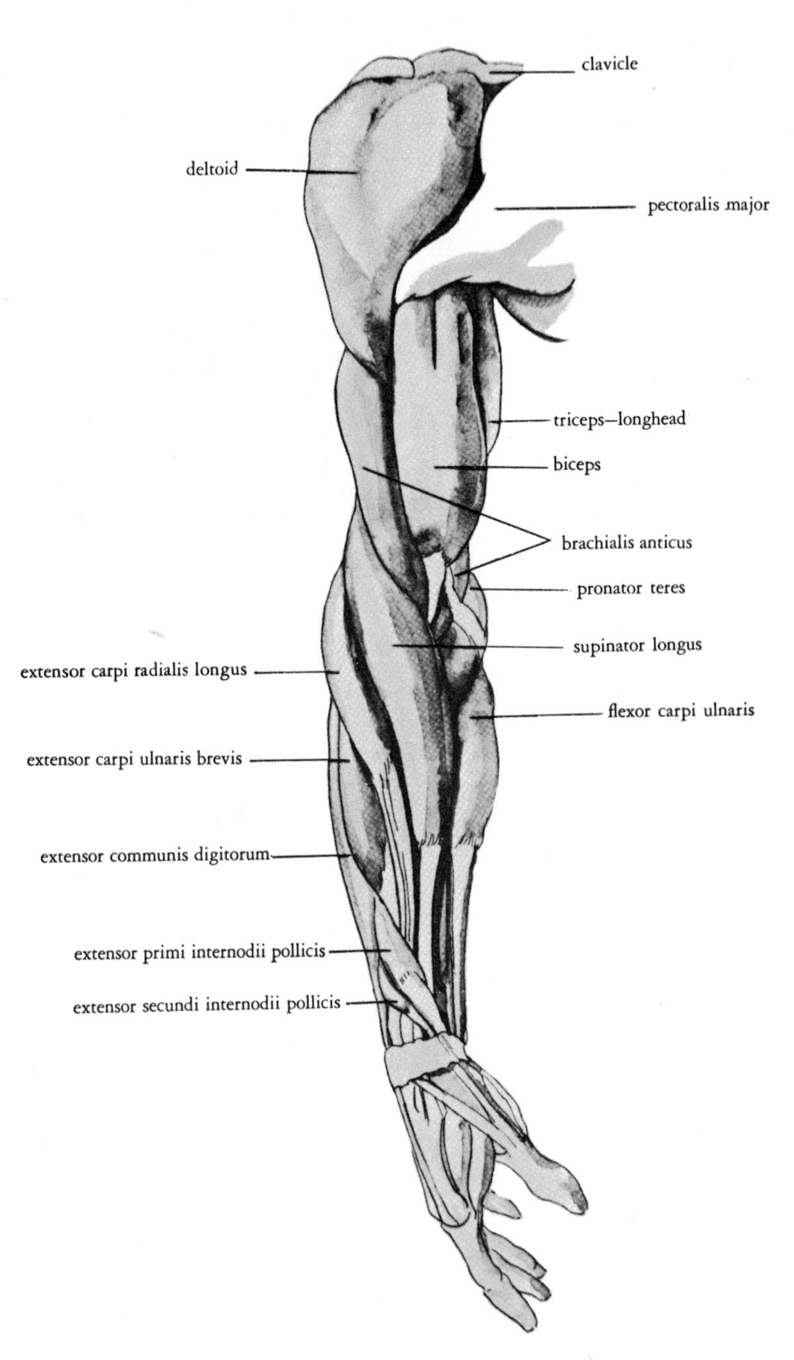
clavicle
deltoid
pectoralis major
triceps—longhead
biceps
brachialis anticus
pronator teres
supinator longus
extensor carpi radialis longus
flexor carpi ulnaris
extensor carpi ulnaris brevis
extensor communis digitorum
extensor primi internodii pollicis
extensor secundi internodii pollicis

FRONT VIEW OF RIGHT ARM

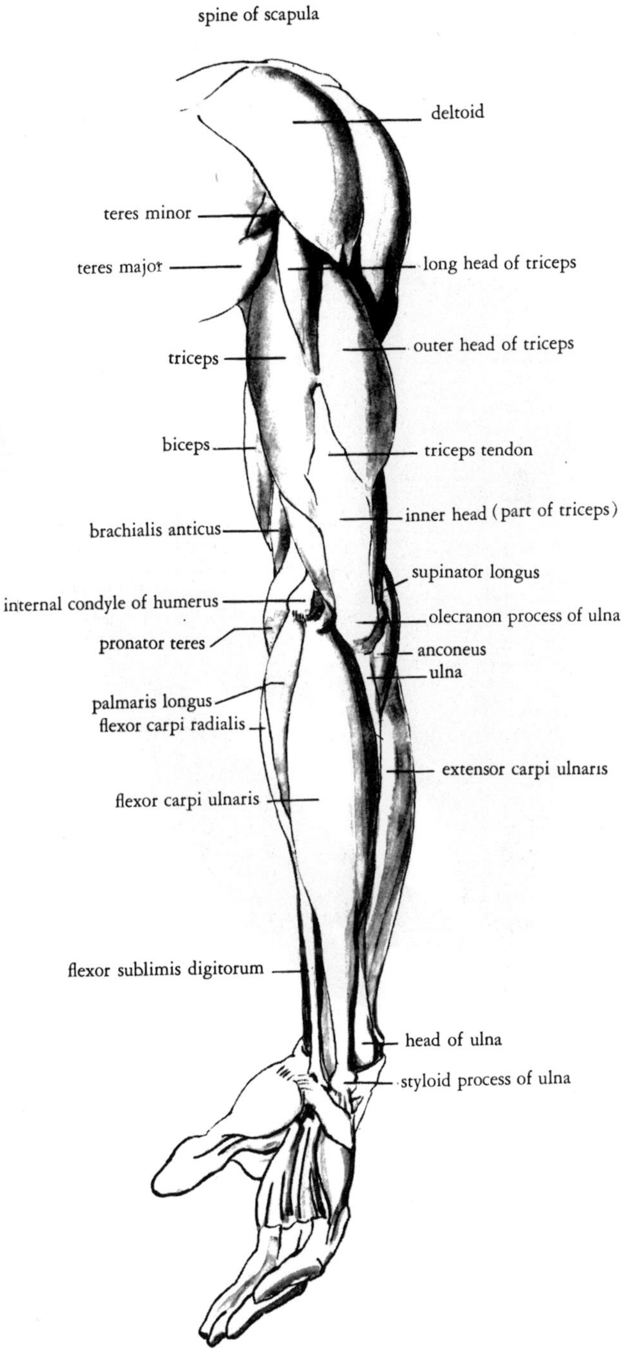

spine of scapula
deltoid
teres minor
teres major
long head of triceps
triceps
outer head of triceps
biceps
triceps tendon
brachialis anticus
inner head (part of triceps)
supinator longus
internal condyle of humerus
olecranon process of ulna
pronator teres
anconeus
ulna
palmaris longus
flexor carpi radialis
extensor carpi ulnaris
flexor carpi ulnaris
flexor sublimis digitorum
head of ulna
styloid process of ulna

BACK VIEW OF ARM

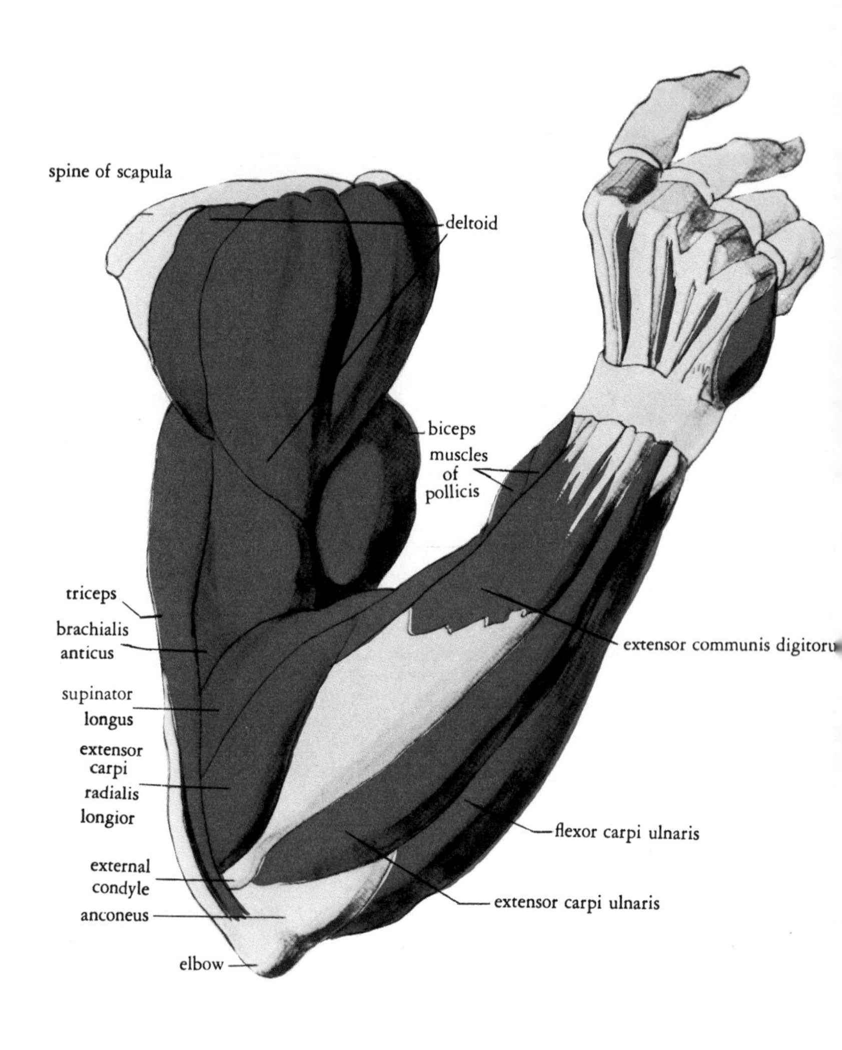
spine of scapula
deltoid
biceps
muscles of pollicis
triceps
brachialis anticus
extensor communis digitoru
supinator longus
extensor carpi radialis longior
flexor carpi ulnaris
external condyle
anconeus
extensor carpi ulnaris
elbow

Arm in Bent Position, Outer View

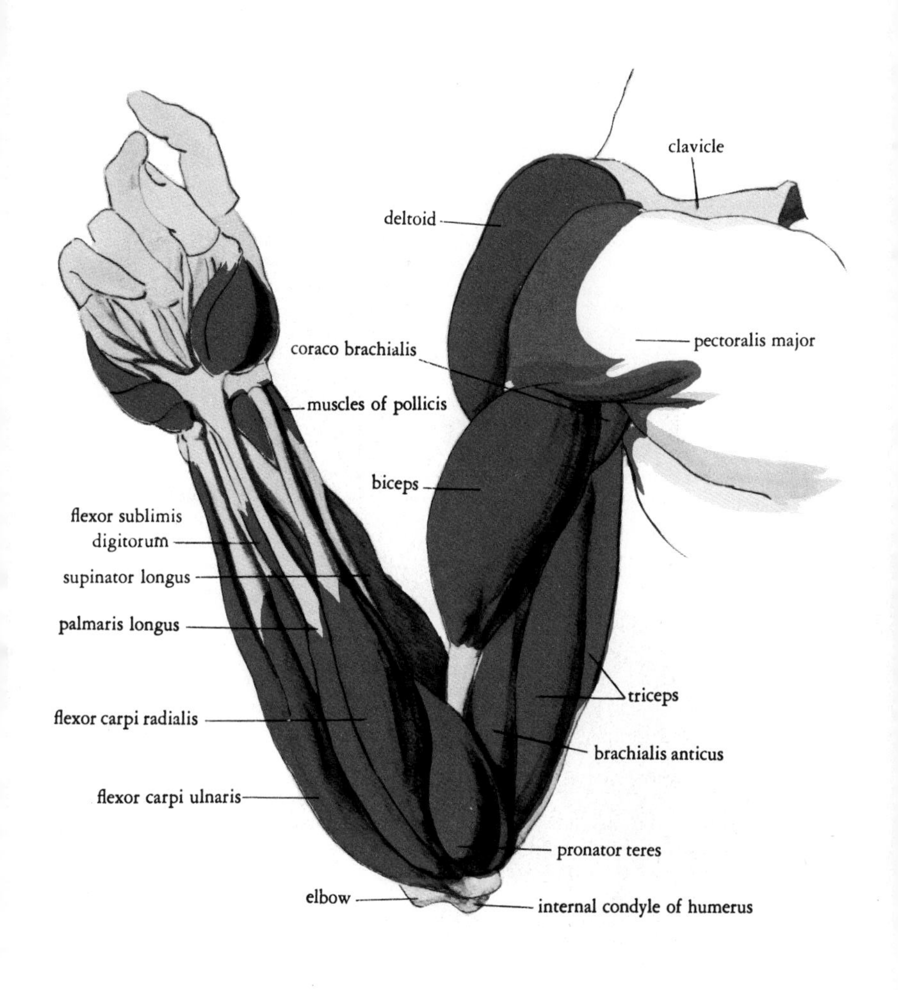
clavicle
deltoid
pectoralis major
coraco brachialis
muscles of pollicis
biceps
flexor sublimis
digitorum
supinator longus
palmaris longus
triceps
flexor carpi radialis
brachialis anticus
flexor carpi ulnaris
pronator teres
elbow
internal condyle of humerus

ARM IN BENT POSITION, INNER VIEW

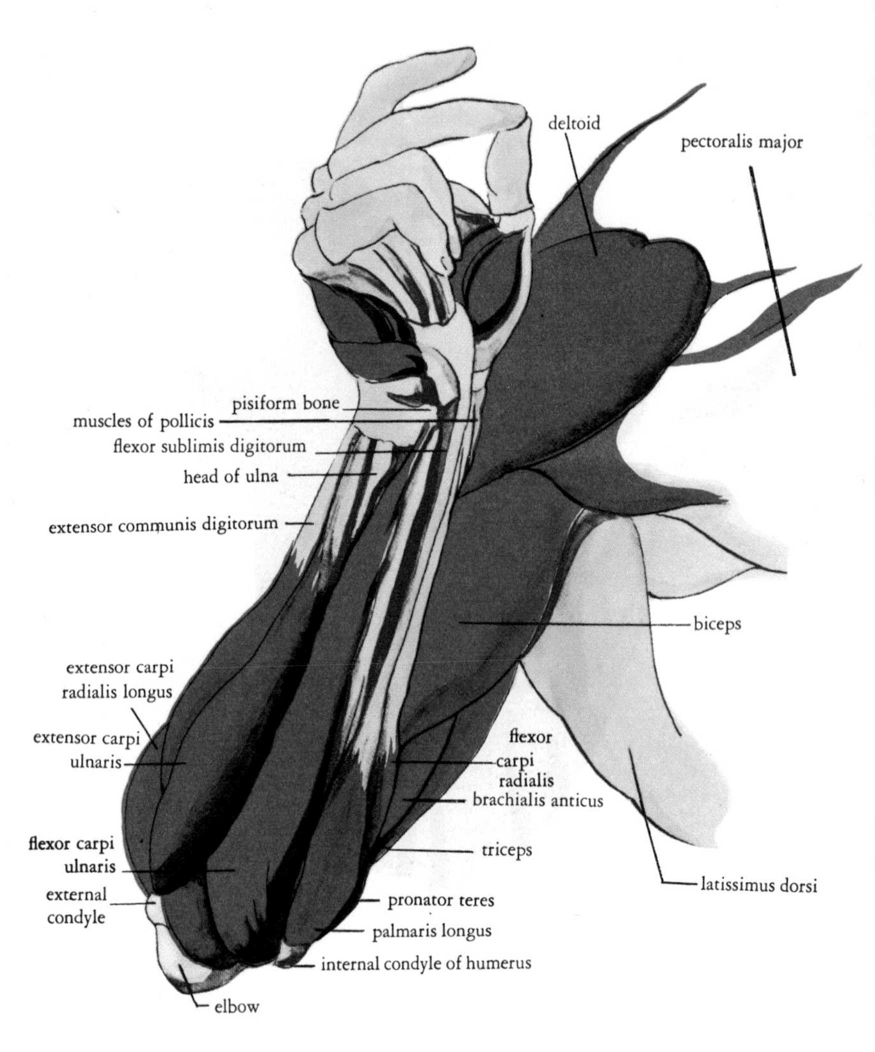
deltoid
pectoralis major
pisiform bone
muscles of pollicis
flexor sublimis digitorum
head of ulna
extensor communis digitorum
biceps
extensor carpi
radialis longus
extensor carpi
ulnaris
flexor
carpi
radialis
brachialis anticus
flexor carpi
ulnaris
triceps
external
condyle
latissimus dorsi
pronator teres
palmaris longus
internal condyle of humerus
elbow

ARM IN BENT POSITION, INNER VIEW

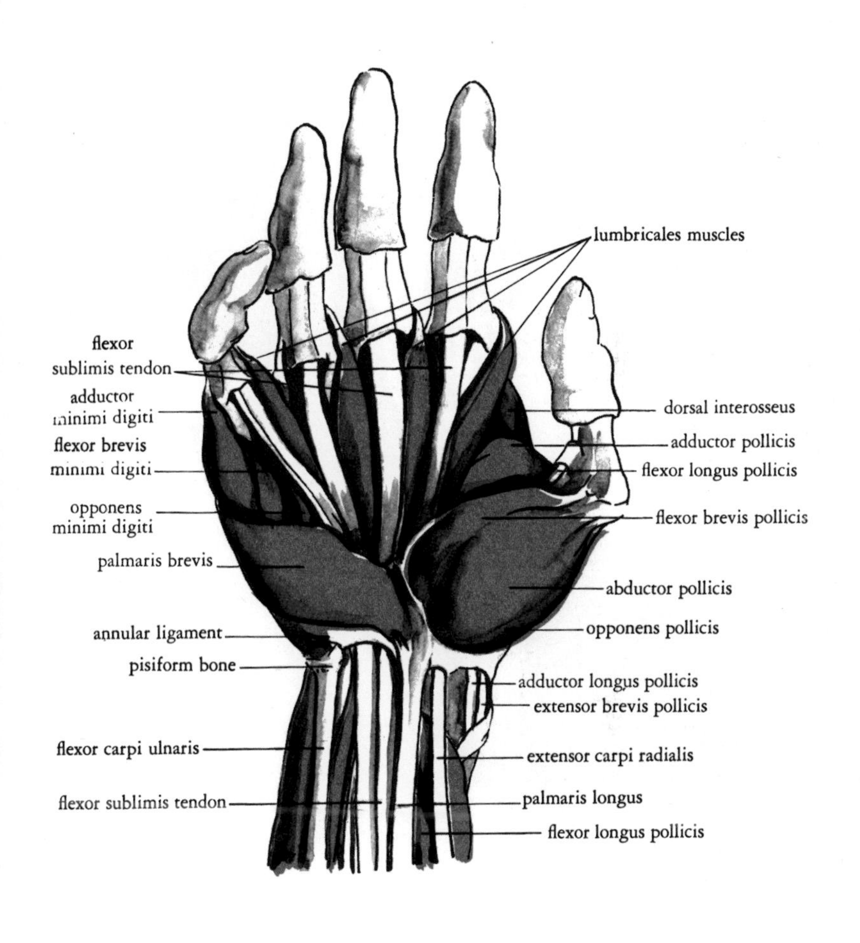
lumbricales muscles
flexor sublimis tendon
adductor minimi digiti
flexor brevis minimi digiti
opponens minimi digiti
palmaris brevis
annular ligament
pisiform bone
flexor carpi ulnaris
flexor sublimis tendon
dorsal interosseus
adductor pollicis
flexor longus pollicis
flexor brevis pollicis
abductor pollicis
opponens pollicis
adductor longus pollicis
extensor brevis pollicis
extensor carpi radialis
palmaris longus
flexor longus pollicis

HAND—PALMAR VIEW

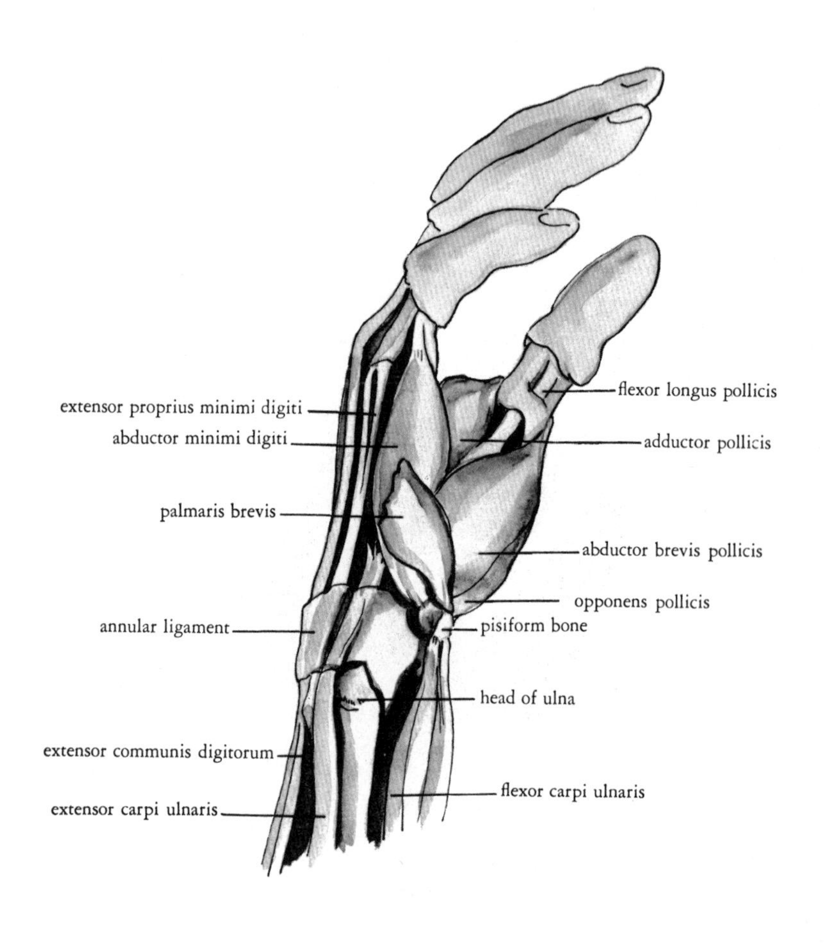
extensor proprius minimi digiti
abductor minimi digiti
palmaris brevis
annular ligament
extensor communis digitorum
extensor carpi ulnaris
flexor longus pollicis
adductor pollicis
abductor brevis pollicis
opponens pollicis
pisiform bone
head of ulna
flexor carpi ulnaris

Outer View of Hand

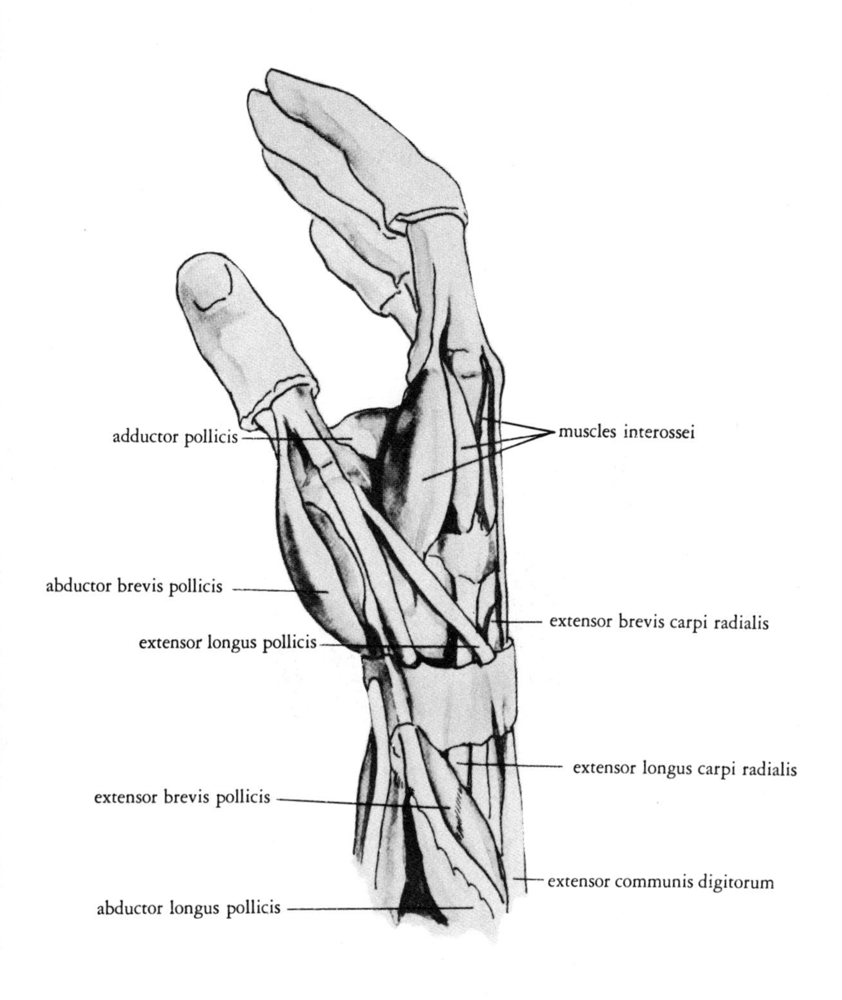
adductor pollicis
muscles interossei
abductor brevis pollicis
extensor brevis carpi radialis
extensor longus pollicis
extensor longus carpi radialis
extensor brevis pollicis
extensor communis digitorum
abductor longus pollicis

Inner View of Hand

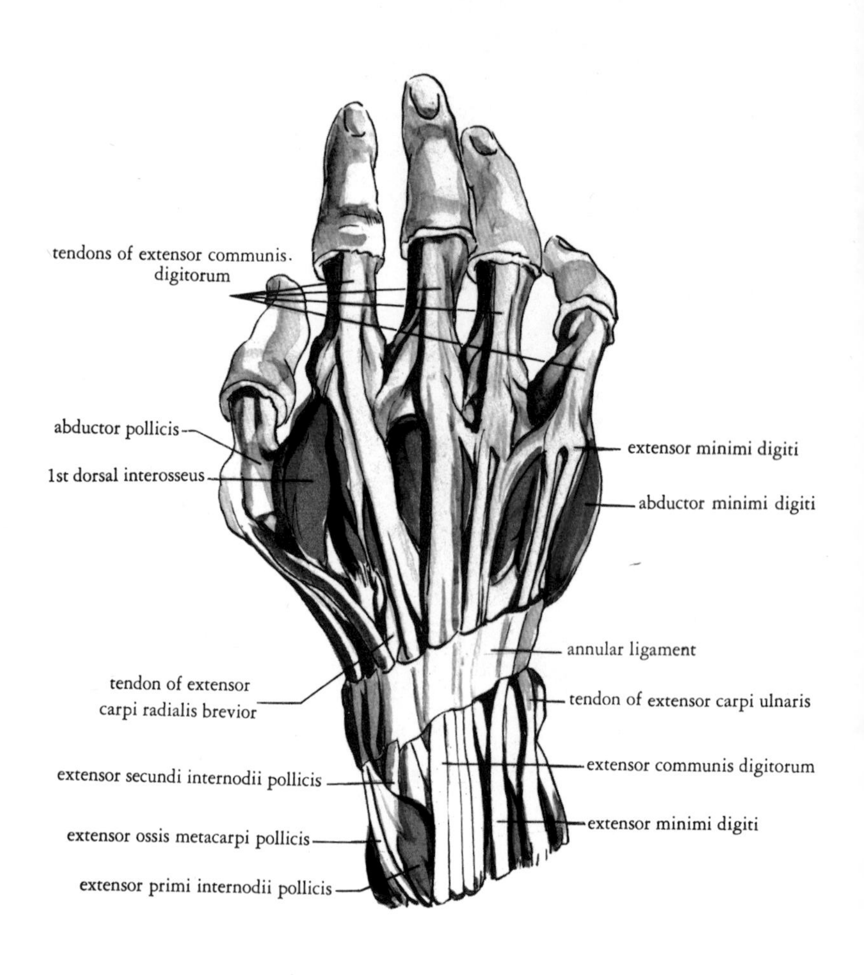
tendons of extensor communis.
digitorum
abductor pollicis
1st dorsal interosseus
extensor minimi digiti
abductor minimi digiti
annular ligament
tendon of extensor
carpi radialis brevior
tendon of extensor carpi ulnaris
extensor secundi internodii pollicis
extensor communis digitorum
extensor ossis metacarpi pollicis
extensor minimi digiti
extensor primi internodii pollicis

Back View of the Hand

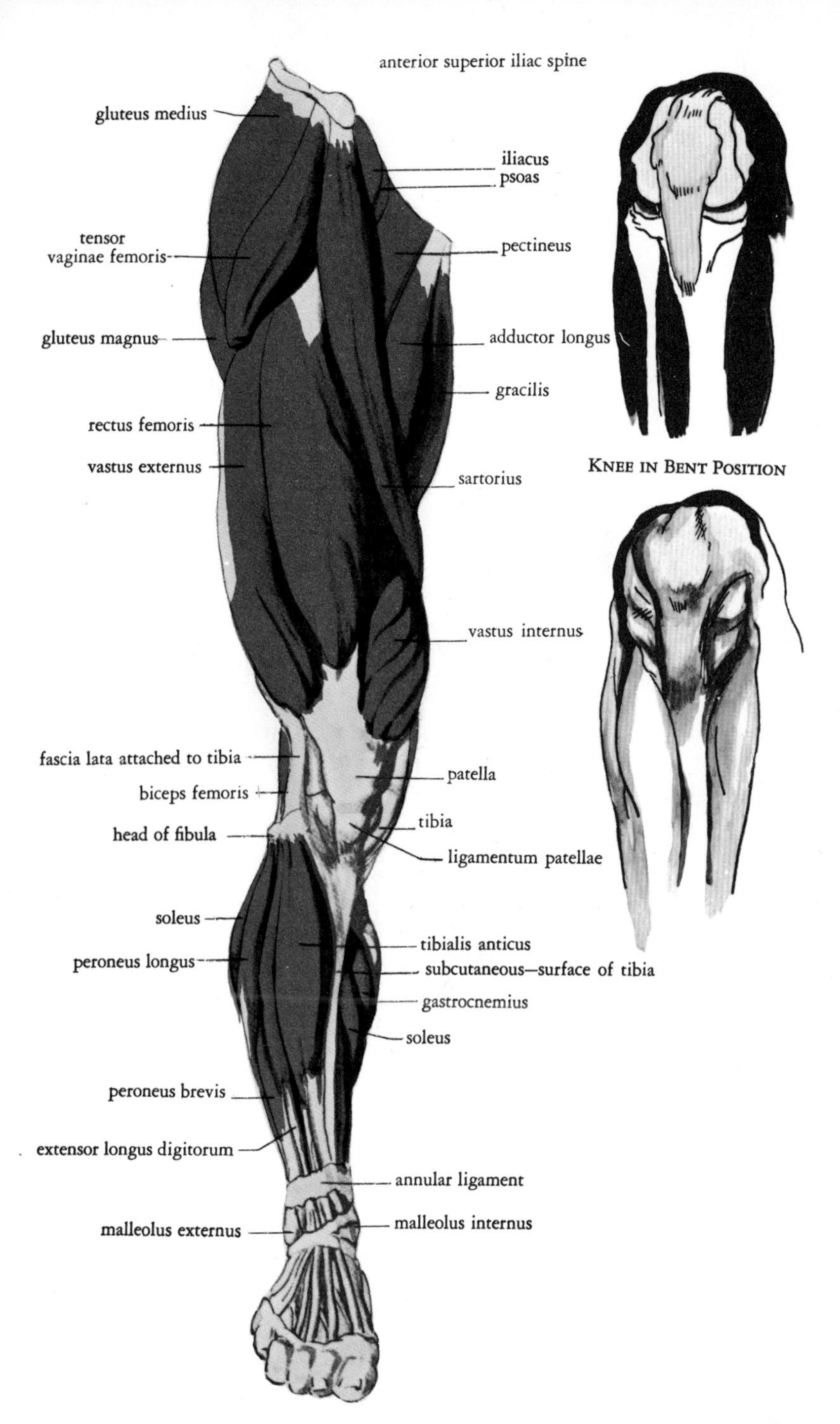
anterior superior iliac spine
gluteus medius
iliacus
psoas
tensor vaginae femoris
pectineus
gluteus magnus
adductor longus
gracilis
rectus femoris
vastus externus
sartorius
vastus internus
fascia lata attached to tibia
patella
biceps femoris
tibia
head of fibula
ligamentum patellae
soleus
tibialis anticus
peroneus longus
subcutaneous—surface of tibia
gastrocnemius
soleus
peroneus brevis
extensor longus digitorum
annular ligament
malleolus internus
malleolus externus

Knee in Bent Position

Leg, Front View

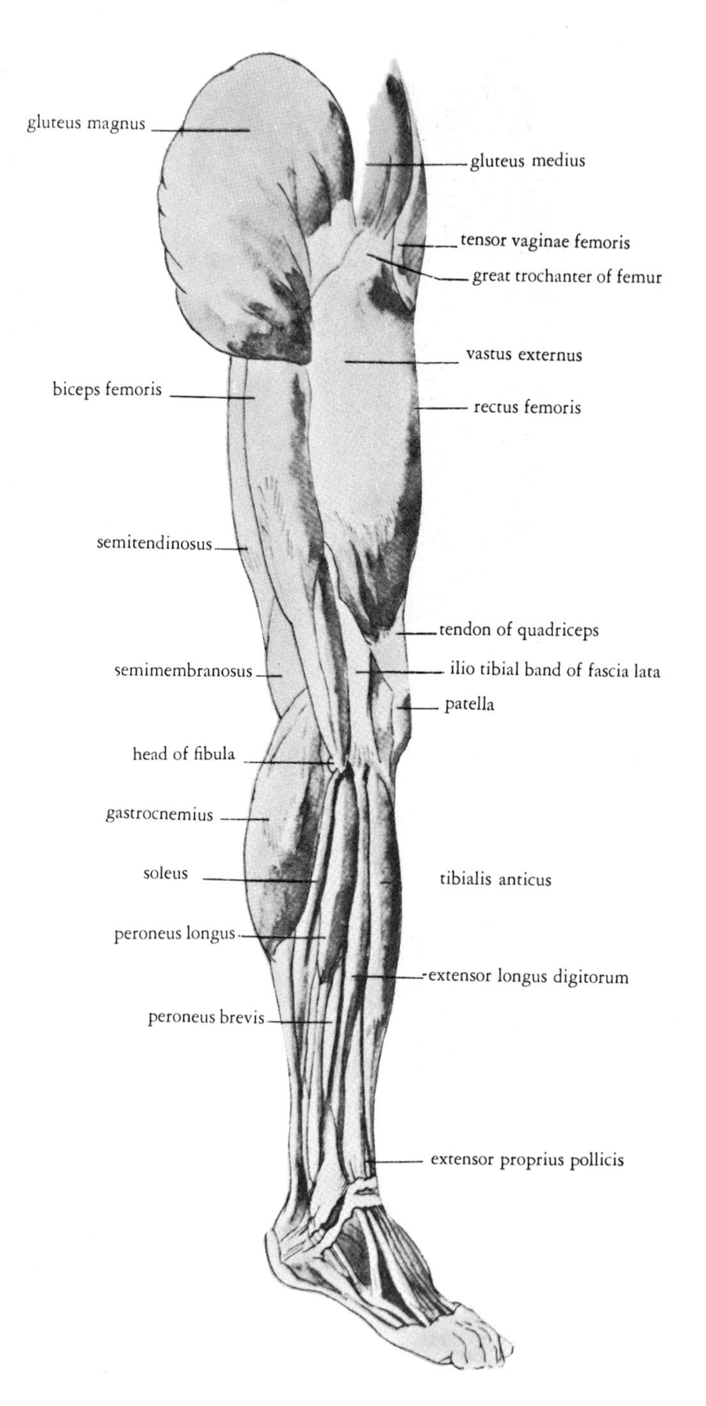
gluteus magnus
gluteus medius
tensor vaginae femoris
great trochanter of femur
vastus externus
biceps femoris
rectus femoris
semitendinosus
tendon of quadriceps
semimembranosus
ilio tibial band of fascia lata
patella
head of fibula
gastrocnemius
soleus
tibialis anticus
peroneus longus
extensor longus digitorum
peroneus brevis
extensor proprius pollicis

Leg, Outer View

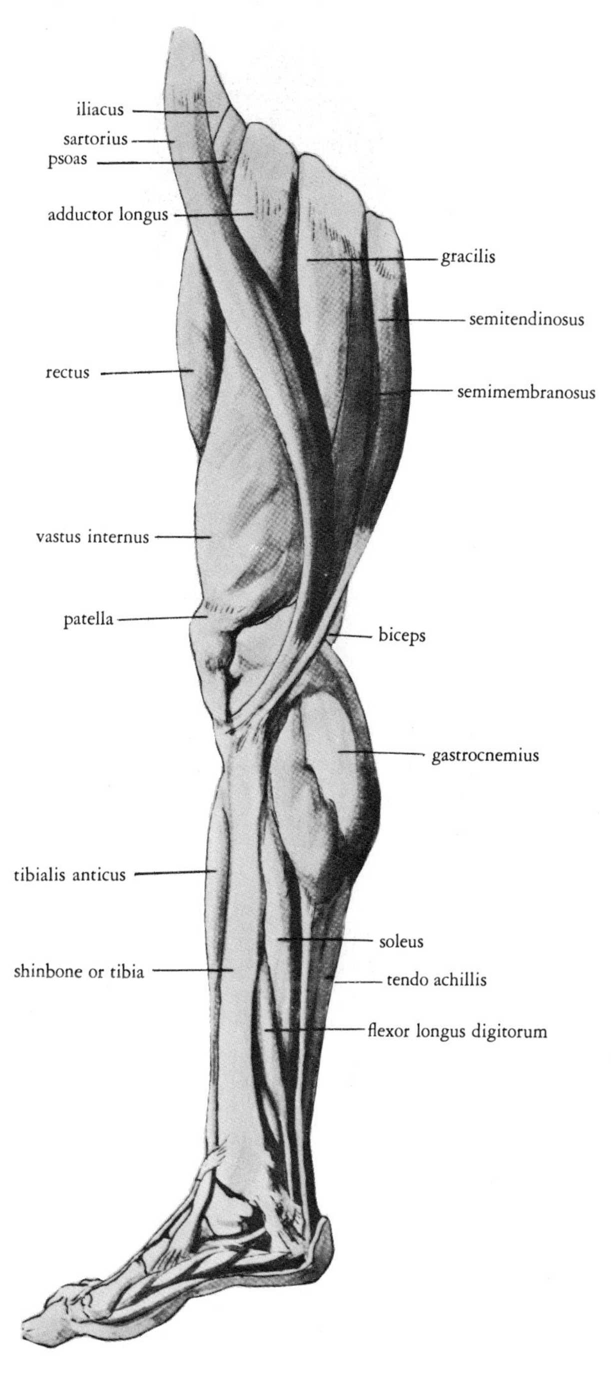
iliacus
sartorius
psoas
adductor longus
gracilis
semitendinosus
rectus
semimembranosus
vastus internus
patella
biceps
gastrocnemius
tibialis anticus
soleus
shinbone or tibia
tendo achillis
flexor longus digitorum

Leg, Inner View

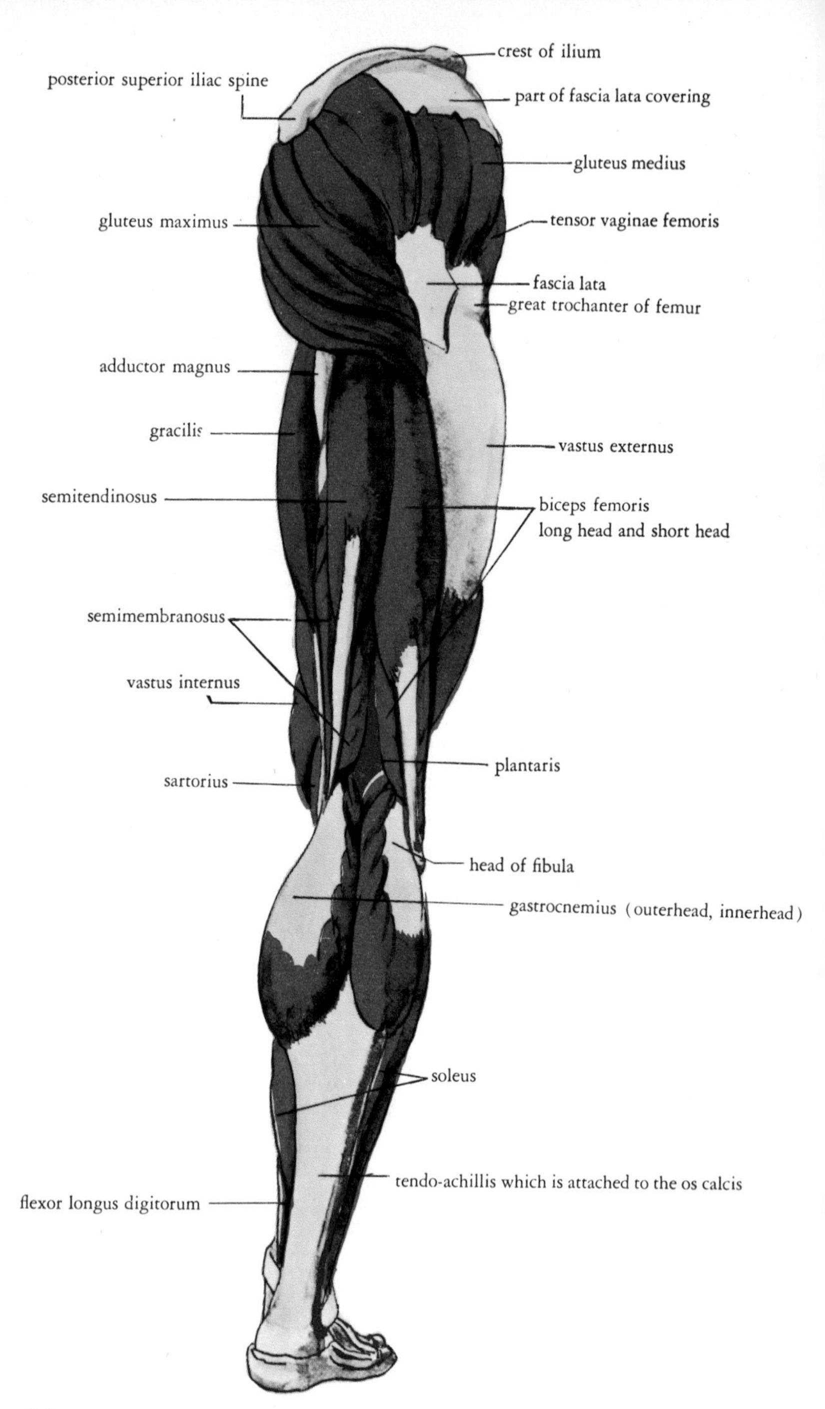
crest of ilium
posterior superior iliac spine
part of fascia lata covering
gluteus medius
gluteus maximus
tensor vaginae femoris
fascia lata
great trochanter of femur
adductor magnus
gracilis
vastus externus
semitendinosus
biceps femoris
long head and short head
semimembranosus
vastus internus
plantaris
sartorius
head of fibula
gastrocnemius (outerhead, innerhead)
soleus
tendo-achillis which is attached to the os calcis
flexor longus digitorum

Leg, Back View

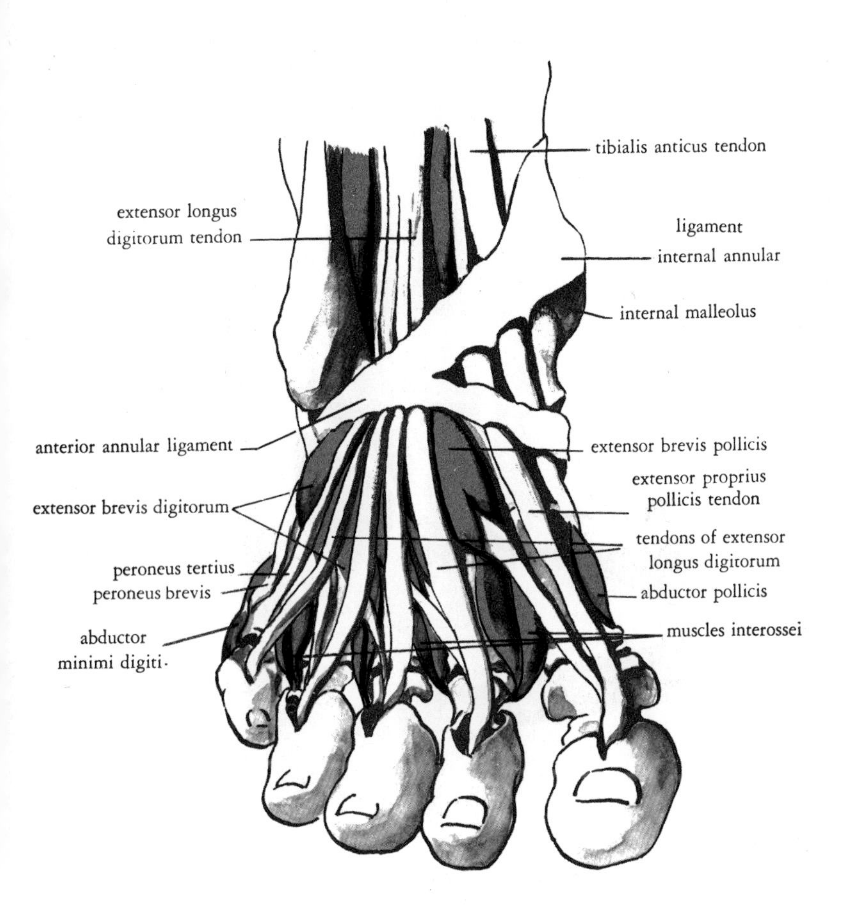
tibialis anticus tendon
extensor longus
digitorum tendon
ligament
internal annular
internal malleolus
anterior annular ligament
extensor brevis pollicis
extensor proprius
pollicis tendon
extensor brevis digitorum
tendons of extensor
longus digitorum
peroneus tertius
peroneus brevis
abductor pollicis
muscles interossei
abductor
minimi digiti

FOOT, FRONT VIEW

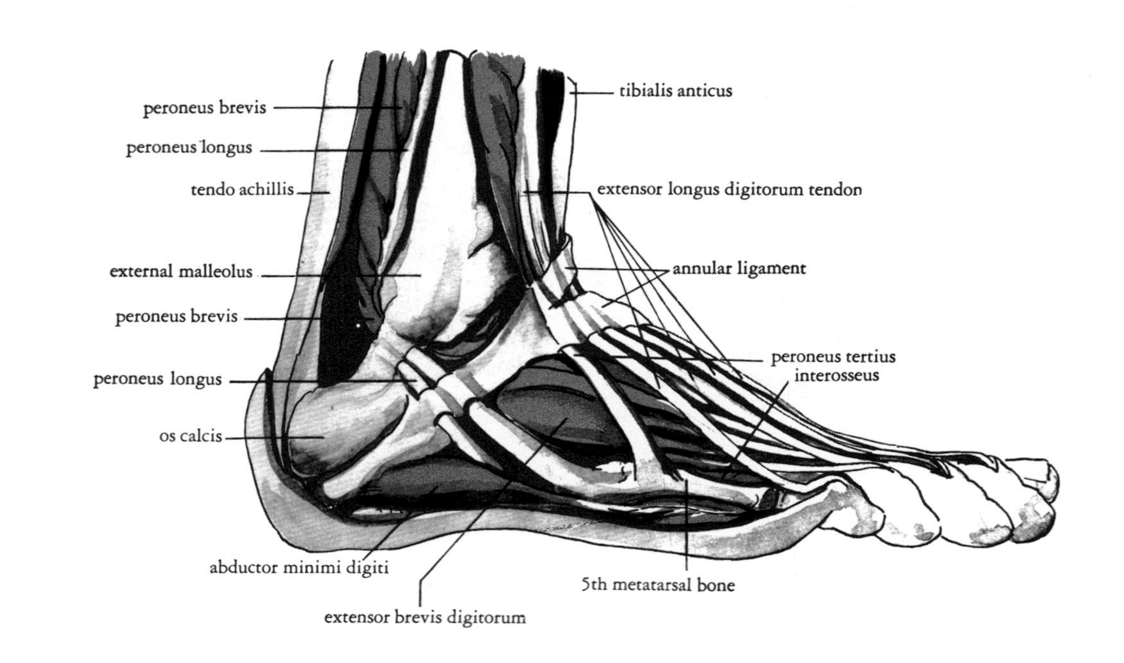
peroneus brevis
peroneus longus
tendo achillis
external malleolus
peroneus brevis
peroneus longus
os calcis
abductor minimi digiti
extensor brevis digitorum
tibialis anticus
extensor longus digitorum tendon
annular ligament
peroneus tertius
interosseus
5th metatarsal bone

Foot, Outer View

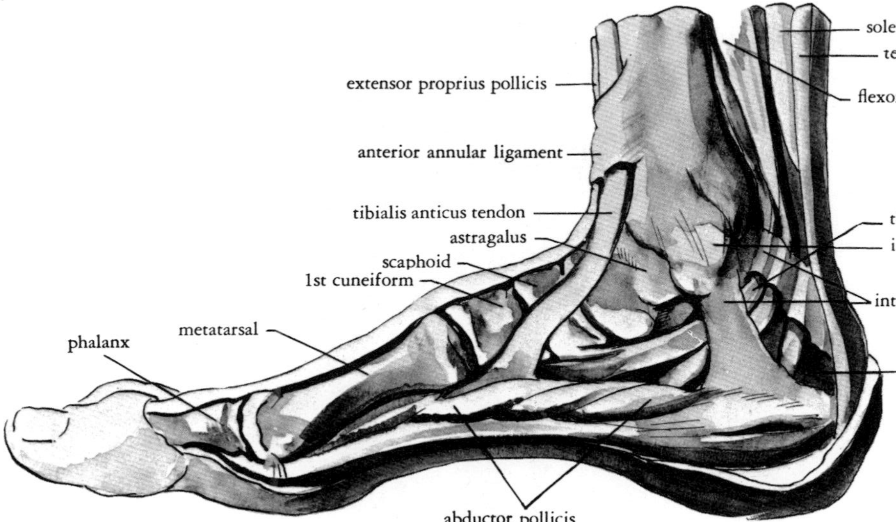

extensor proprius pollicis
anterior annular ligament
tibialis anticus tendon
astragalus
scaphoid
1st cuneiform
metatarsal
phalanx
soleus
tendo achillis
flexor longus pollicis
tibialis posticus
internal malleolus
internal annular ligament
os calcis
abductor pollicis

Foot, Inner View

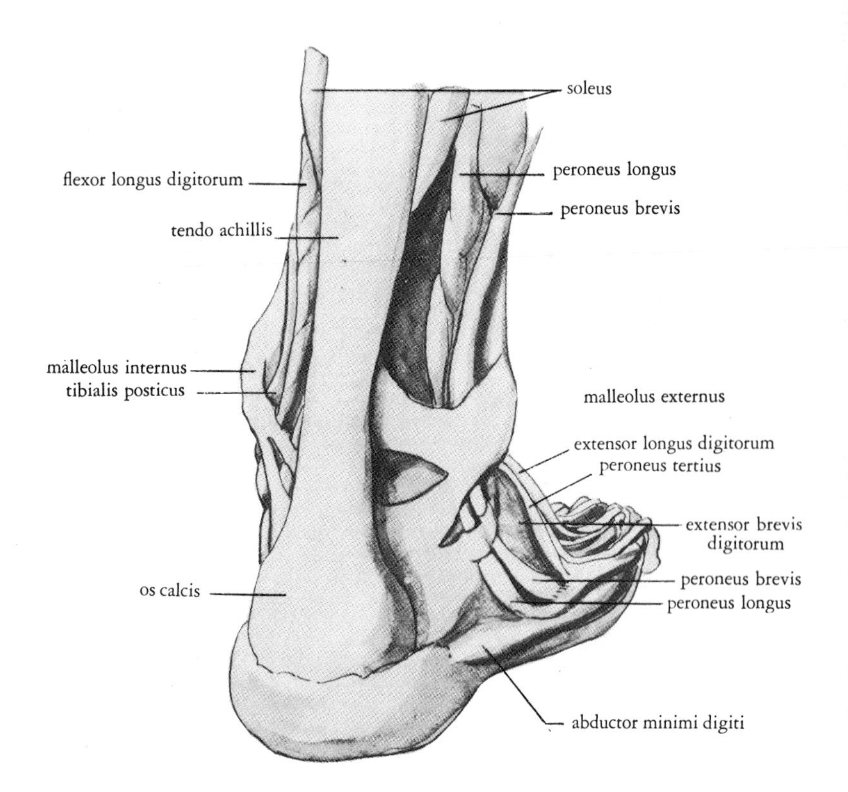
soleus
flexor longus digitorum
peroneus longus
peroneus brevis
tendo achillis
malleolus internus
tibialis posticus
malleolus externus
extensor longus digitorum
peroneus tertius
extensor brevis digitorum
peroneus brevis
os calcis
peroneus longus
abductor minimi digiti

Foot, Back View

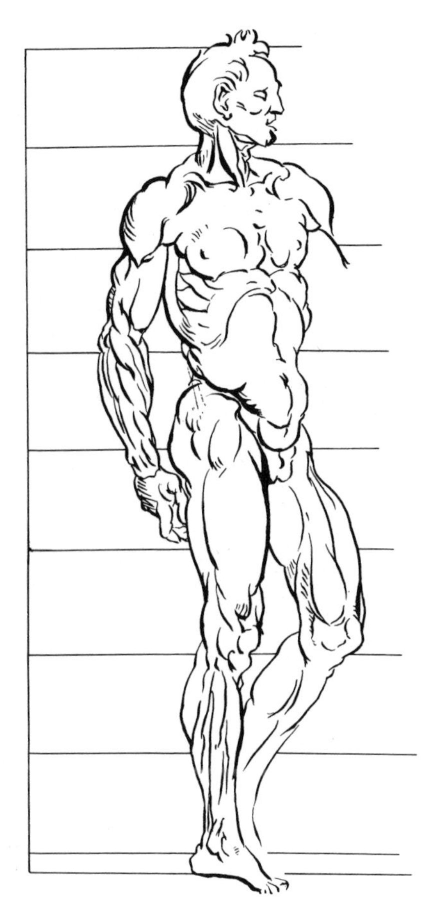

PROPORTIONS
(AFTER MICHELANGELO BUONAROTTI 1475-1564)

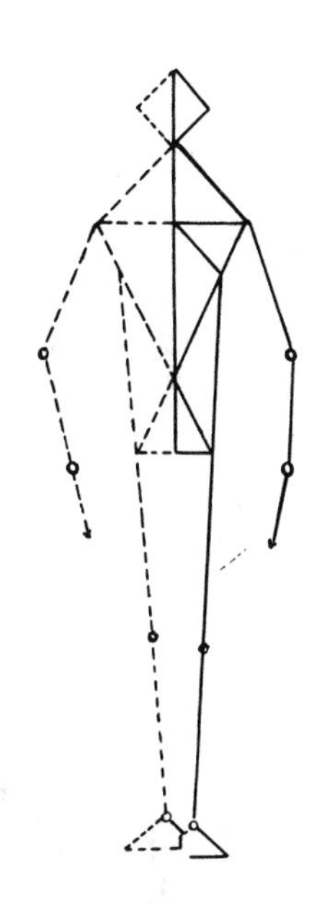

THE GOLDEN CUT (*Goldener Schnitt*)

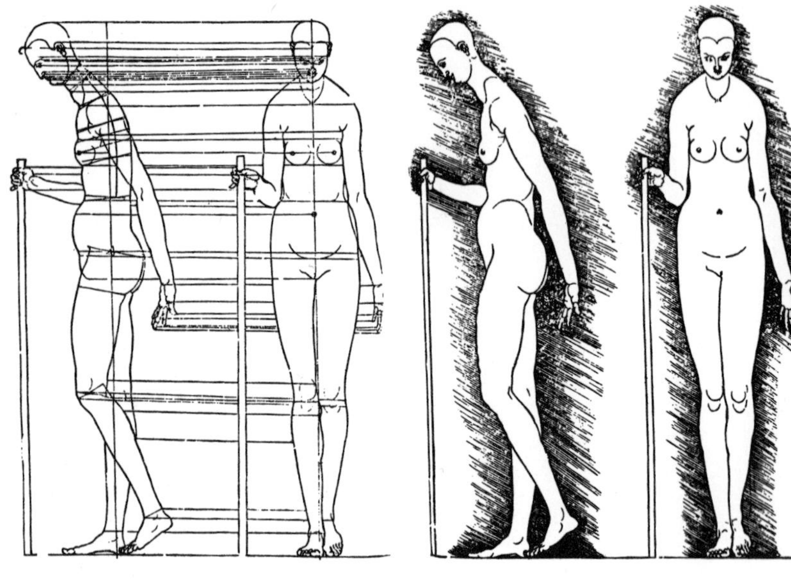

CONSTRUCTIONS OF A FEMALE NUDE (ALBRECHT DUERER 1471-1528)

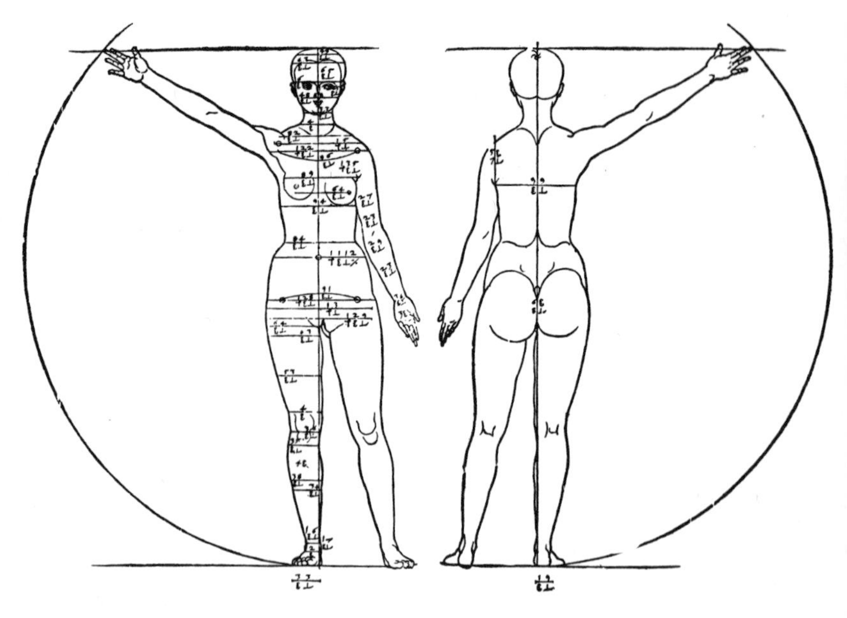

PROPORTIONS OF THE FEMALE BODY (ALBRECHT DUERER 1471-1528)

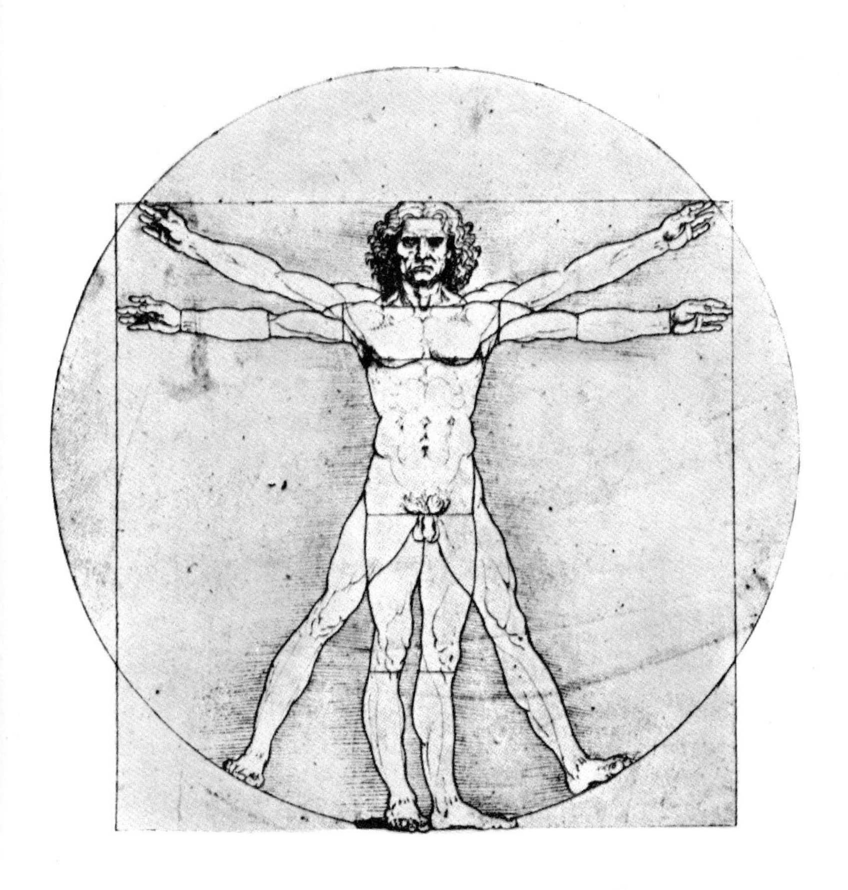

The Proportions of the Human Figure after Vitruvius
(Leonardo da Vinci 1452-1519)

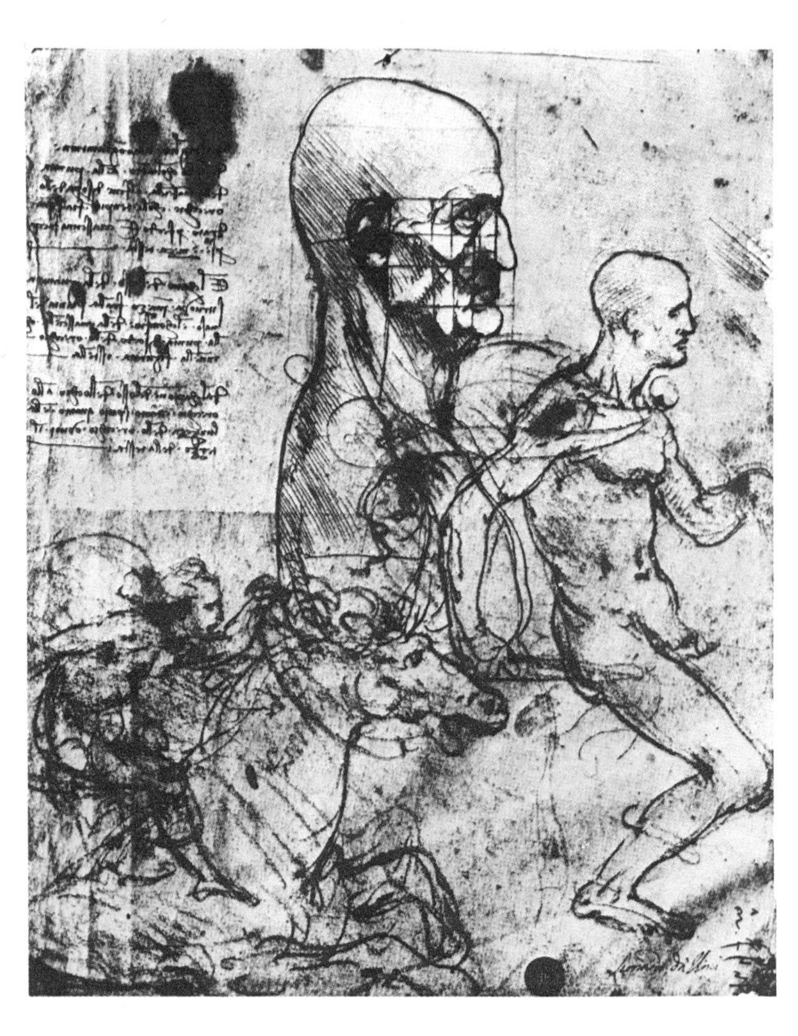

Head Proportions and Sketch of Horsemen

(Leonardo da Vinci 1452-1519)

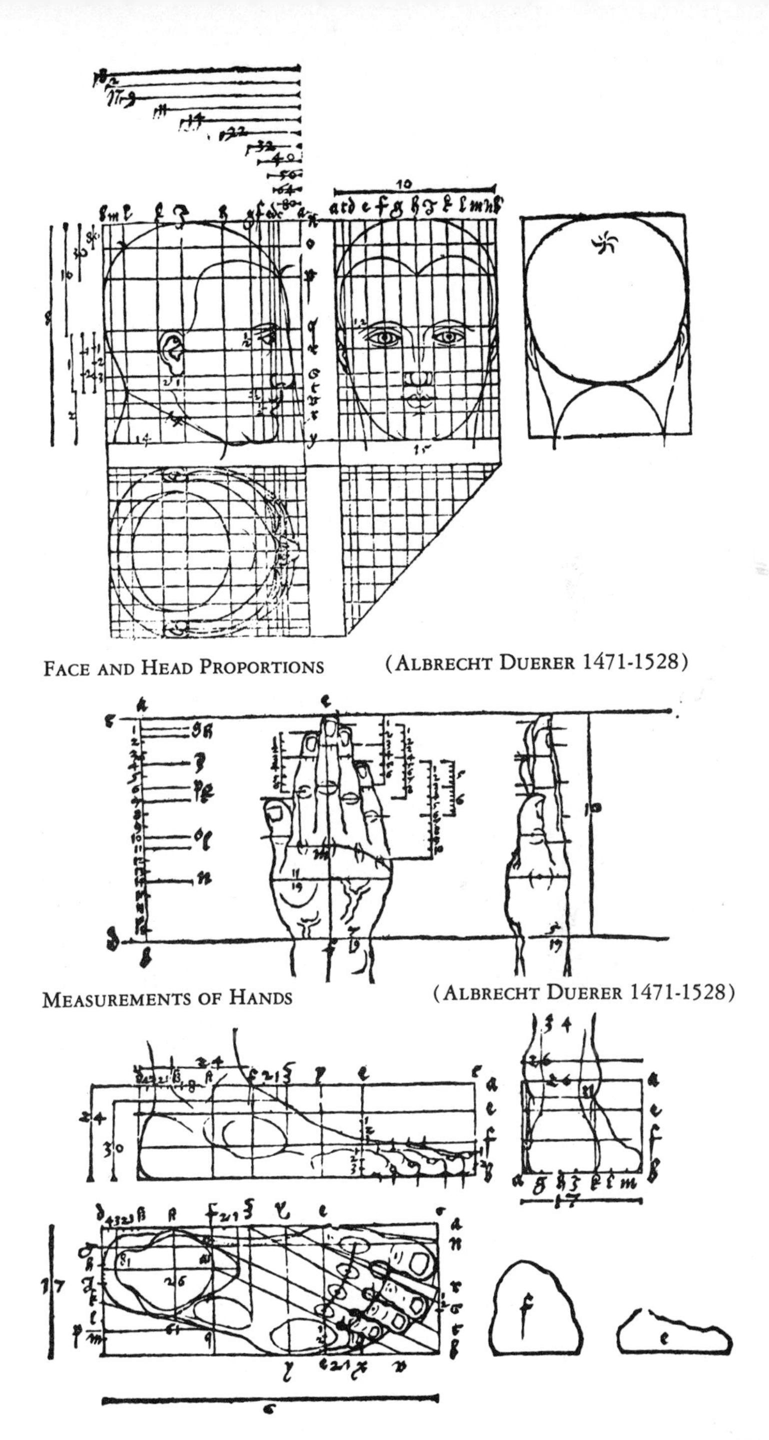

Face and Head Proportions (Albrecht Duerer 1471-1528)

Measurements of Hands (Albrecht Duerer 1471-1528)

Measurements of Feet (Albrecht Duerer 1471-1528)

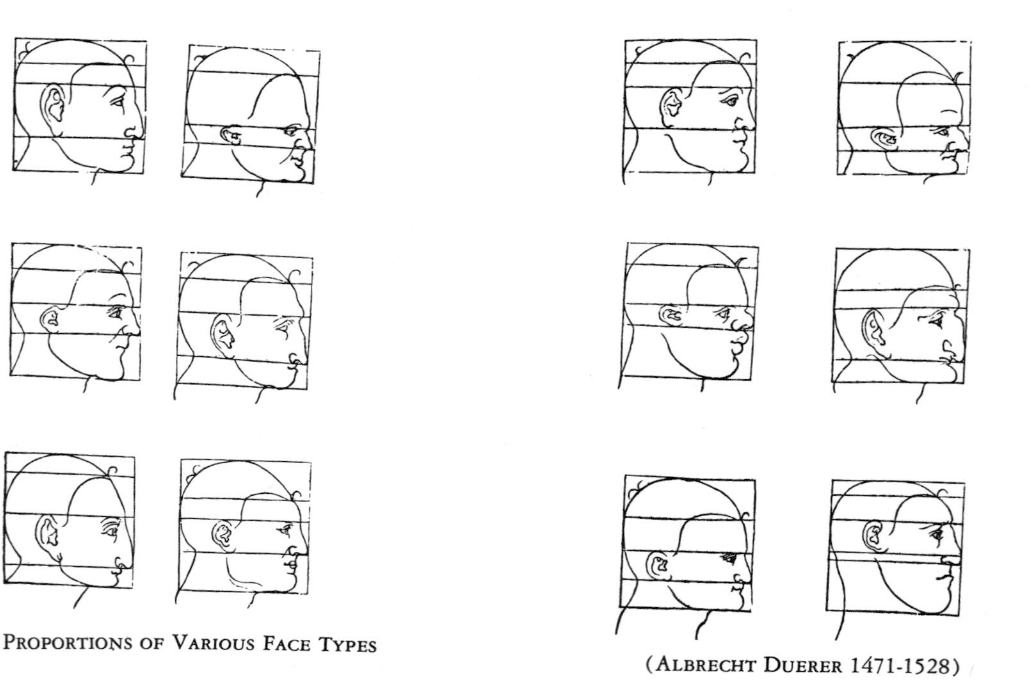

Proportions of Various Face Types

(Albrecht Duerer 1471-1528)

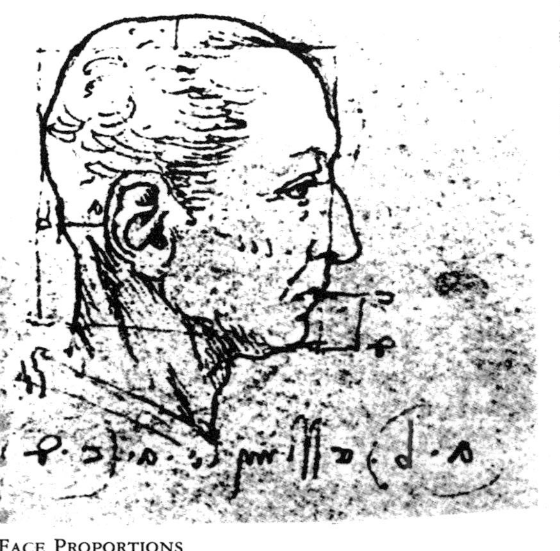

Face Proportions

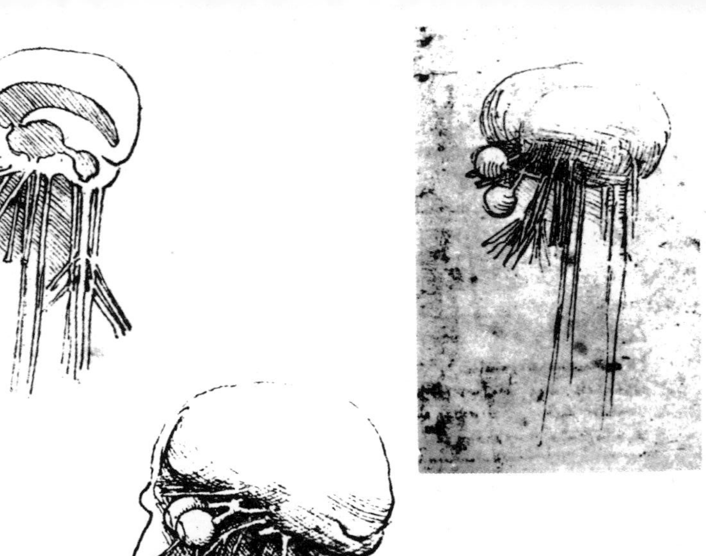

Studies of the Human Eye (Leonardo da Vinci 1452-1519)

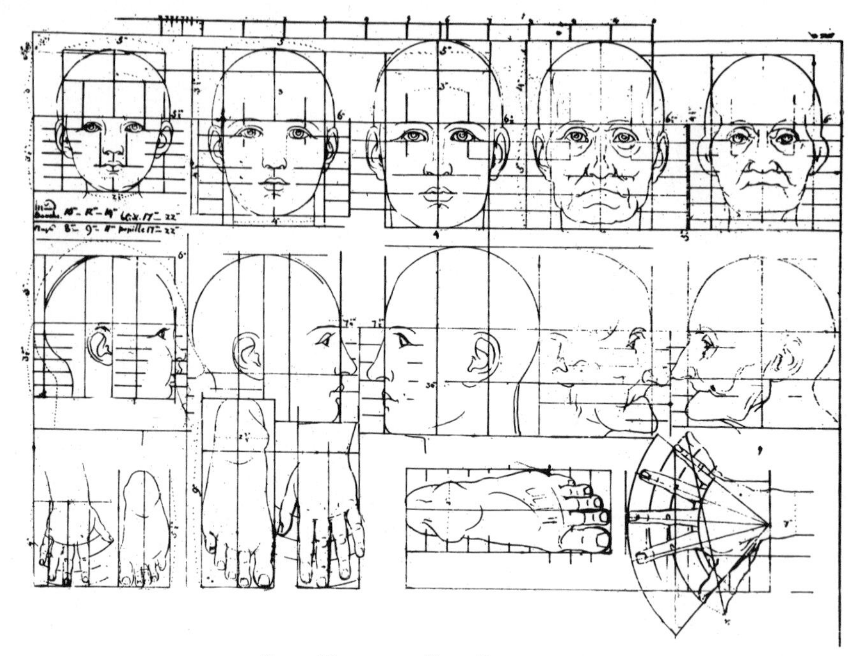

FACE, HAND AND FEET PROPORTIONS

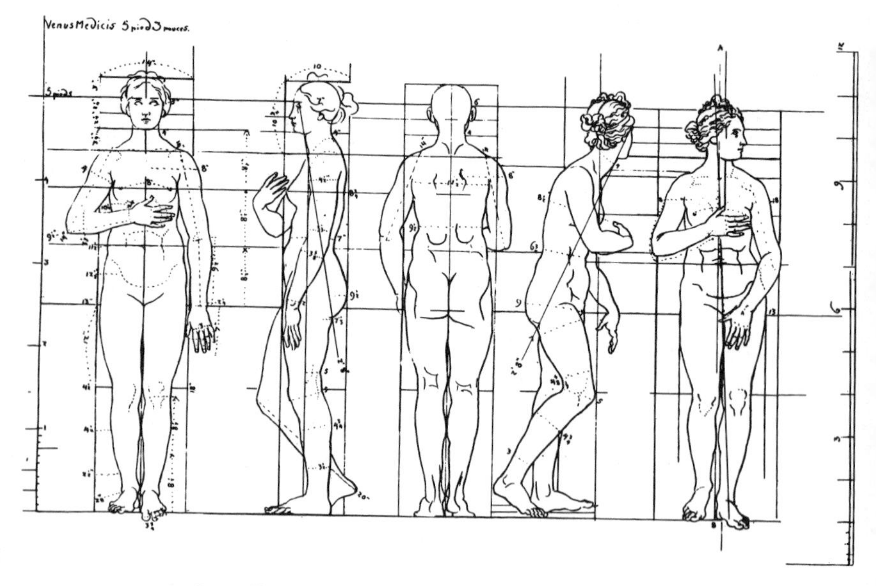
VenusMedicis 5pied3pouces.

SOME PROPORTIONS OF THE MALE AND FEMALE BODY

(JOHANN GOTTFRIED SCHADOW 1764-1850)

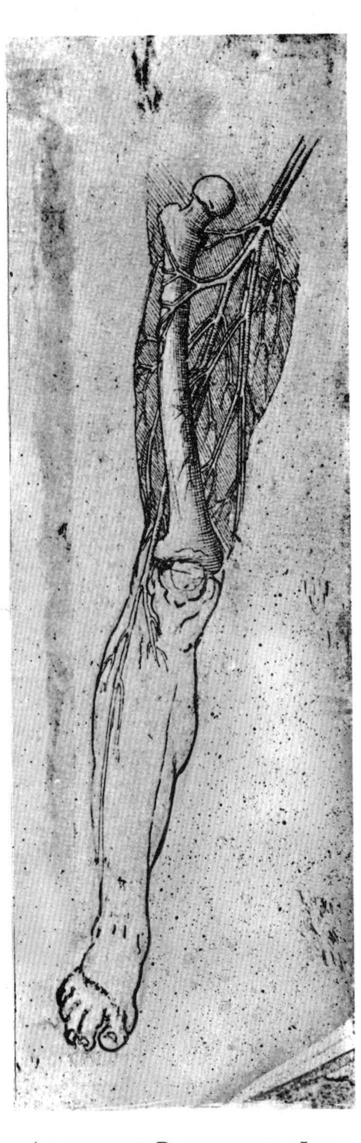

Anatomical Drawing of a Leg

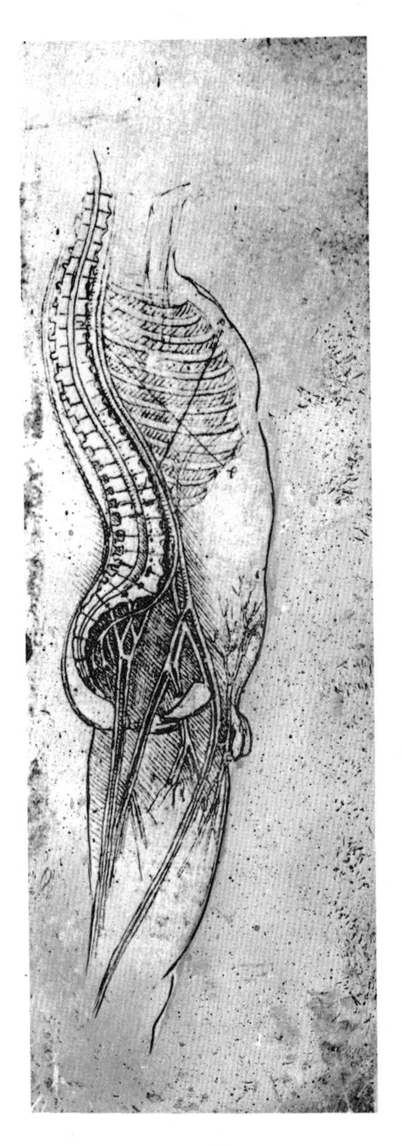

Anatomical Drawing of the Vertebral Column

(Leonardo da Vinci 1452-1519)

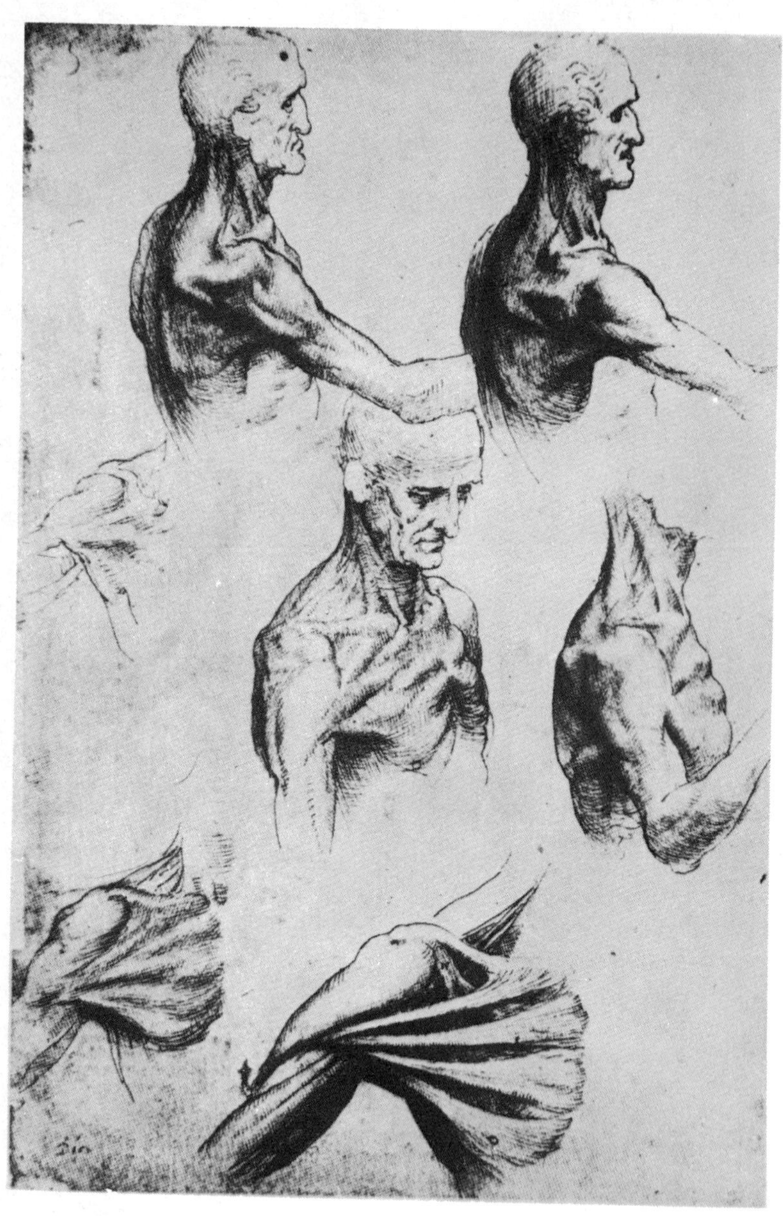

Anatomical Studies of the Pectoralis—Major and Arm Muscles
(Leonardo da Vinci 1452-1519)